# *Hot Rock Guitar Gr*

## Introductions, Information & Appendices

- *Welcome To Hot Rock Guitar Grade 3*    3
- *Introduction To Tone*    4
- *Guitar Notation Explained*    119

### Van Halen | 'Ain't Talkin' 'Bout Love'

- *Factfile*    7
- *Exam Version*    8
- *Walkthrough*    10
- *Full Transcription*    40
- *Notes*    51

### Black Sabbath | 'Paranoid'

- *Factfile*    23
- *Exam Version*    24
- *Walkthrough*    26
- *Full Transcription*    82
- *Notes*    87

### Oasis | 'Cigarettes and Alcohol'

- *Factfile*    11
- *Exam Version*    12
- *Walkthrough*    14
- *Full Transcription*    52
- *Notes*    61

### Kings of Leon | 'Sex On Fire'

- *Factfile*    27
- *Exam Version*    28
- *Walkthrough*    30
- *Full Transcription*    88
- *Notes*    95

### Razorlight | 'Golden Touch'

- *Factfile*    15
- *Exam Version*    16
- *Walkthrough*    18
- *Full Transcription*    62
- *Notes*    69

### The Raconteurs | 'Steady, As She Goes'

- *Factfile*    31
- *Exam Version*    32
- *Walkthrough*    34
- *Full Transcription*    96
- *Notes*    103

### Jimi Hendrix Experience | 'Hey Joe'

- *Factfile*    19
- *Exam Version*    20
- *Walkthrough*    22
- *Full Transcription*    70
- *Notes*    81

### Metallica | 'Wherever I May Roam'

- *Factfile*    35
- *Exam Version*    36
- *Walkthrough*    38
- *Full Transcription*    104
- *Notes*    117

Evergreen House, 2-4 King Street, Twickenham, Middlesex TW1 3RZ

*www.rockschool.co.uk*

# Acknowledgements

rockschool would like to thank all the people who worked on this book. We would particularly like to thank our colleagues at Music Sales Ltd who granted us licences to print the music and who did such a great job on the audio.

| | |
|---|---|
| Published by: | rockschool Ltd. © rockschool Ltd 2011 – *www.rockschool.co.uk* |
| | under license from Music Sales Ltd |
| Compiled and edited by: | James Uings, Simon Pitt, Simon Troup and Jeremy Ward |
| Full Transcriptions provided by: | Music Sales Ltd |
| Music engraving: | Simon and Jennie Troup – *www.digitalmusicart.com* |
| | |
| Cover design: | Petra Hamarova – *www.fuelcreativity.com* |
| Layout and internal design: | Simon Troup – *www.digitalmusicart.com* |
| Cover Photography: | © Corbis – *www.corbis.com* |
| Internal Photography: | © Getty Images – *www.gettyimages.co.uk* |
| | |
| Printed in the UK: | Caligraving Ltd, Brunel Way, Thetford, Norfolk, IP24 1HP |
| CD Manufacturing: | brandedmedia Ltd – *www.brandedmedia.net* |
| | |
| Exclusive Distributors: | Music Sales Ltd, Newmarket Road, Bury St Edmunds, Suffolk, IP33 3YB |
| | – *www.musicroom.com* |
| | |
| Audio Producer: | Tom Farncombe, Music Sales Ltd |
| Audio Engineer: | Jonas Persson, Music Sales Ltd |
| Mixing and mastering: | Jonas Persson, Music Sales Ltd |
| | |
| Musicians: | Arthur Dick *(Guitar)* |
| | Paul Townsend *(Bass on all songs except 'Golden Touch')* |
| | Tom Farncombe *(Bass on 'Golden Touch')* |
| | Noam Lederman *(Drums on all songs except 'Golden Touch'* |
| | *and 'Cigarettes and Alcohol')* |
| | Brett Morgan *(Drums on 'Cigarettes and Alcohol')* |
| | Chris Baron *(Drums on 'Golden Touch')* |
| | Paul Honey *(Keyboards)* |
| | Jonas Persson *(Keyboards)* |
| | |
| Legal Information: | *rockschool, the rockschool logo and all other rockschool product* |
| | *or service names are trademarks of rockschool Ltd* |

# Welcome to Hot Rock Guitar Grade 3

Welcome to Hot Rock Grade 3 for Guitar. This book of classic and contemporary rock tracks has been compiled to give you a resource to help you develop your guitar skills and performance chops.

The songs in their edited forms can be used as Free Choice Pieces in the rockschool Guitar Grade 3 exam. Alternatively, you can use either the edited or the full versions in the performance units in public exams such as GCSEs or A Levels. You can, of course, enjoy playing the tracks for their own sake.

Hot Rock Guitar Grade 3 contains eight top songs covering the range of rock performers over the last forty years. It is divided into two sections. The first section is made up of eight chapters. Each chapter is based around a version of a well-known track that has been specially edited to make it Grade 3 standard. The full transcription of each song is printed in the second half of the book.

Accompanying the book are two CDs of specially recorded backing tracks featuring all live instruments. The first CD contains performances of the edited pieces along with a backing track.

The second CD contains performances of the fully transcribed pieces, along with backing tracks for you to practise along to. Both CDs have count-ins on the backing tracks and the full mixes.

A word about musical notation: we refer throughout the book to quarter notes, eighth notes, sixteenth notes etc rather than crotchets, quavers and semiquavers.

We hope that you enjoy playing these pieces. You can find further details about rockschool's guitar and other instrumental syllabuses visiting our website at **www.rockschool.co.uk**.

# Introduction To Tone

A large part of an effective guitar performance is selecting the right tone. The electric guitar's sound is subject to a wide range of variables. This guide outlines the basic controls present on most amplifiers as well as the common variations between models. There is also a basic overview of pickups and the effect their location on the guitar has on the guitar's tone. Finally, it covers the differences between the distortion types – crucial to getting your basic sound right.

At Grade 3 you are only expected to use one tone throughout the song and you are not expected to use any additional effects units, though you may use them if you wish.

## Basic amplifier controls

Most amplifiers come with a standard set of controls that are the same as, or very similar to, the diagram below. It's important to understand what each control is and the effect it has on your guitar's tone.

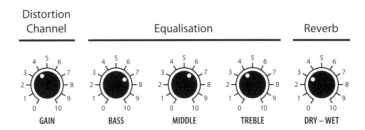

- **Channel (Clean/Distortion)**

  Most amplifiers have two channels, which can be selected by either a switch on the amp or a footswitch. One channel is usually 'clean' while the other can be driven harder to create a distorted (or 'dirty') tone. If your amp doesn't have two channels, look at 'variations of basic controls' to see how to get clean and dirty tones from a single channel amp.

- **Gain**

  In simple terms the gain determines how hard you drive the amp. This governs how distorted the dirty (also called 'drive', 'overdrive' or 'distortion') channel is and acts as a second volume control on the clean channel (though a high gain setting will distort even the clean channel).

- **Bass**

  This adjusts the lowest frequencies. Boost it to add warmth and reduce or 'cut' it if your sound is muddy or woolly.

- **Middle**

  This is the most important equalisation (often shortened to just 'EQ') control. Most of the guitar's tone character is found in the midrange, so adjusting this control has a lot of impact on your tone. Boosting it with a dirty sound will give a more classic rock sound, while cutting it will produce a more metal tone.

- **Treble**

  This adjusts the high frequencies. Boost it to add brightness and cut it if the sound is too harsh or brittle.

- **Reverb**

  Short for 'reverberation'. This artificially recreates the ambience of your guitar in a large room, usually a hall. This dial controls the balance between the 'dry' (the sound without the reverb) and 'wet' (the sound with the reverb) sounds.

## Variations of basic controls

The diagram above shows the most common amp controls. There are many variations to this basic setup which can be confusing. The following section is a breakdown of some of the other amp controls you may encounter.

- **Presence control**

  Sometimes this dial replaces the 'middle' control and sometimes it appears in addition to it. It adjusts the higher midrange frequencies (those found between the 'middle' and 'treble' dials).

### ▪ No reverb control
Reverb can be a nice addition to your guitar tone, but it is not essential. Don't be concerned if your amp does not have a reverb control.

### ▪ Volume, gain, master setup
Single channel amplifiers often have an extra volume control (in addition to the master volume) located next to the gain control. For clean sounds keep the gain set low and the volume similarly low and use the master control for overall volume. If the master control is on 10 and you require more level, turn the volume control up, though you may find this starts to distort as you reach the higher numbers.

To get a distorted tone turn the volume down low and the gain up till you get the amount of distortion you require. Regulate the overall level with master volume. As before, if the master control is on 10 and you require more level, turn the volume up. In this case, however, you may find you lose clarity before you reach maximum.

## Pickups
Entire books have been devoted to the intricacies of pickups. However, three basic pieces of information will help you understand a lot about your guitar tone:

### ▪ Singlecoils
Singlecoils are narrow pickups that you'll see fitted to many guitars. The Fender Stratocaster is the most famous guitar fitted with singlecoils. They produce a bright, cutting sound that can sound a little thin in some situations, especially heavier styles of rock music.

### ▪ Humbuckers
Humbuckers were originally designed to remove or 'buck' the hum produced by singlecoil pickups, hence the name 'humbuckers'. They produce a warm, mellow sound compared to singlecoil pickups, but have a tendency to sound a little muddy in some situations. They are usually identifiable because they are twice the width of a singlecoil pickup. The Gibson Les Paul is a well-known guitar that is fitted with humbucking pickups.

### ▪ Pickup location
Pickups located near the guitar's neck will have the warmest sound, while pickups located near the bridge will have the brightest sound.

## Different types of 'dirty' tones
There are lots of different words to describe the 'dirty' guitar sounds. In fact, all the sounds are 'distortions' of the clean tone, which can be confusing when you consider there's a 'type' of distortion called 'distortion'! Below is a simplified breakdown of the three main types of dirty sounds and some listening material to help you through this tonal minefield.

### ▪ Overdrive
This is the 'mildest' form of distortion. It can be quite subtle and only evident when the guitar is played strongly. It can be also be full-on and aggressive.
*Hear it on:* Cream – 'Sunshine Of Your Love', AC/DC – 'Back In Black', Oasis – 'Cigarettes and Alcohol'.

### ▪ Distortion
Distortion is usually associated with heavier styles of music. It is dense and the most extreme of the dirty tones and usually associated with heavy styles of music.
*Hear it on:* Metallica – 'Enter Sandman', Avenged Sevenfold – 'Bat Country', Bon Jovi – 'You Give Love A Bad Name'.

### ▪ Fuzz
As the name implies fuzz is a broken, 'fuzzy' sound. It was very popular in the 60s, but while still popular, is less common now.
*Hear it on:* Jimi Hendrix Experience – 'Purple Haze', The Kinks – 'You Really Got Me'.

# Examination Versions

These examination versions are arranged from the original songs. While adjustments have been made to the arrangements to make the pieces playable at Grade 3 and make them appropriate as examination pieces, we have worked hard to maintain the integrity and spirit of the original music.

Aside from the arrangement, the examination versions differ in that the backing tracks generally only contain bass, drums and, where appropriate, keyboards. This keeps the examination versions in line with the band setup found on the rockschool graded examination pieces.

The accompanying audio for these arrangements can be found on CD1. There are two tracks for each song. The first is the full performance including the guitar part, while the second is the backing track without the guitar part. The backing tracks should be used in examinations.

The edited part is printed over two pages and is preceded by a 'Fact File' detailing information about the song, the band and the guitarist who played on it and some 'Recommended Listening' if you wish to research the artist further. At the end of each chapter there is a 'Walkthrough', giving you tips on how to play the piece and any technical challenges to look out for as you practise.

We have also included some general advice on getting an authentic tone for each track, including suggested amp settings. Treat these as a guide to point you in the right direction, rather than a strict set of instructions that must be slavishly followed: guitar and amplifier sounds differ significantly, so the right setup for one guitar may not be the correct setup for another. Your ears should always be the final judge about whether something sounds good or not. If you require more information on amplifiers and their controls, pickups and guitar tones in general, please refer to the 'Introduction To Tone' section on pages 4 & 5.

*© Ethan Miller | Getty Images Entertainment*

SONG TITLE: AIN'T TALKIN' 'BOUT LOVE
ALBUM: VAN HALEN
RELEASED: 1978
LABEL: WARNER BROTHERS
GENRE: CLASSIC ROCK

PERSONNEL: EDDIE VAN HALEN (GTR)
DAVID LEE ROTH (VOX)
MICHAEL ANTHONY (BASS)
ALEX VAN HALEN (DRUMS)

UK CHART PEAK: N/A
US CHART PEAK: N/A

© Jon Sievert | Premium Archive

## BACKGROUND INFO

The main riff to 'Aint Talkin' Bout Love' is based on muted Am, F and G arpeggios. The guitar is treated with a slow flanger effect. This formed part of Eddie Van Halen's so-called 'Brown Sound' which helps make the riff even more distinctive. This riff forms the backbone for the whole song: all the other sections are essentially variations of this basic idea.

## THE BIGGER PICTURE

It's impossible to understate the impact had Eddie Van Halen on rock guitar playing. Apart from Jimi Hendrix, no one has influenced more guitarists than Van Halen. His exciting, flamboyant style, spearheaded by his amazing two-handed tapping technique is second to none: *Van Halen* and *Van Halen II* are considered essential listening for everyone serious about the guitar.

## NOTES

Although he's credited for *popularising* the often-emulated tapping technique, Eddie Van Halen would be the first to admit he didn't invent it. Steve Hackett can be heard tapping arpeggios at the start of the Genesis song, 'The Return Of The Giant Hogweed' from the 1971 album *Nursey Cryme* and Jeff Beck used tapped notes to create a yodelling sound. Van Halen has stated he got the idea from watching Led Zeppelin guitarist Jimmy Page play his unaccompanied solo in 'Heartbreaker'. Page played a hammer-on and pull-off lick that made use of open strings. Van Halen worked out that he could transpose the pattern elsewhere on the neck by using his picking hand to help the stretch.

## RECOMMENDED LISTENING

*Van Halen* is full of astonishing guitar playing. 'Eruption' is explosive from start to finish, including the famous triplet tapping pattern, and is one of the most famous guitar tracks of all time. 'I'm The One' is a high tempo boogie, while the cover of the Kinks' song 'You Really Got Me' features yet more guitar pyrotechnics. The follow up 1979's, *Van Halen II* features the nylon string cadenza 'Spanish Fly', which is the acoustic cousin of 'Eruption'. 'Outta Love Again' features pinched hamonics in the riff and a tasteful solo that's a perfect example of Van Halen's impeccable phrasing. 1984's album, *1984,* saw the band take a more poppy direction, but Eddie's outstanding playing can still be heard on the frenetic 'Hot For Teacher' and the massive hit 'Jump'.

# Ain't Talkin' 'Bout Love

## Van Halen

Words & Music by David Lee Roth, Edward Van Halen, Alex Van Halen & Michael Anthony

♩=139 *Classic Rock*

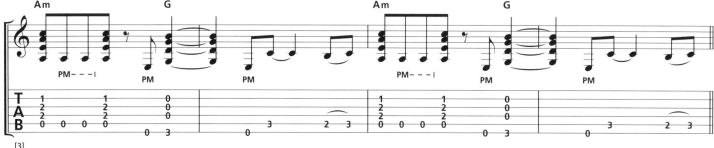

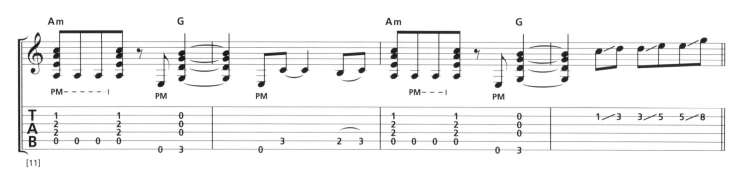

**Guitar Solo**

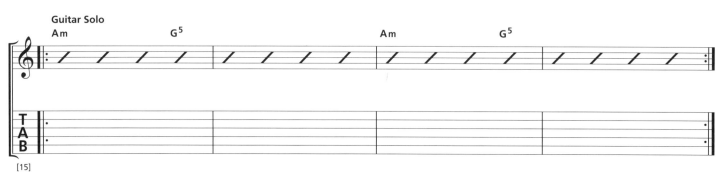

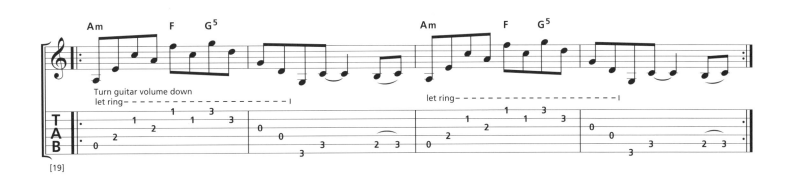

[19]

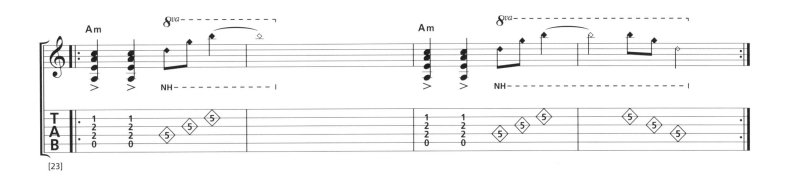

[23]

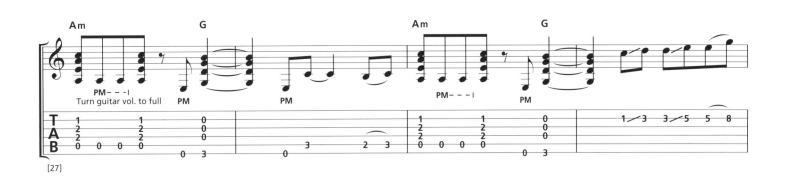

[27]

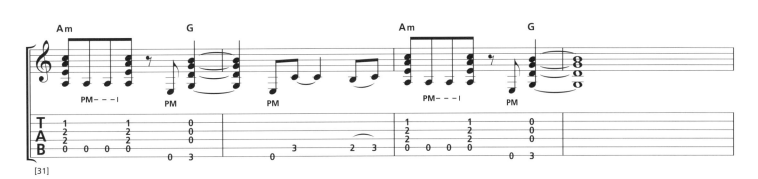

[31]

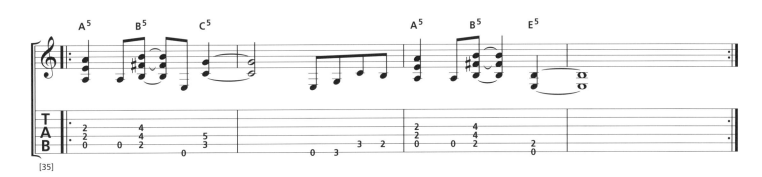

[35]

# Walkthrough

## Tone

The original version of 'Ain't Talkin' 'Bout Love' uses a phaser effect pedal. However, at Grade 3 you are not expected to use effects pedals. Aim for a modern hi-gain distortion and boost the middle and treble to help the guitar cut through and add some bite to the tone.

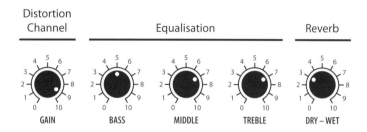

## Intro & Chorus 1 (Bars 1–6)

The solo guitar intro is a palm-muted riff based on the Am, F and G arpeggios. The final part of the riff uses notes from the A natural minor scale. The chorus is a variation of the intro riff which uses strummed chords instead of arpeggios.

### Bars 1–2 | *Palm muting*

Place the edge of the right side of your palm on the lowest sounding strings to lightly mute the strings. Be careful not to move your hand too far from the bridge as this may raise the pitch of the note. Take extra care if your guitar has a floating bridge (where the bridge is tensioned to 'float above the guitar's body) because pressing too hard will push the bridge down and raise the pitch of the notes.

### Bars 3–6 | *Down stroke picking*

This riff is best played using all down strokes as this provides the solid attack and consistency required (Fig. 1).

## Verse & Chorus 2 (Bars 7–14)

The verse is another variation of the intro riff. This time the G chord is brought forward a beat and played as a two-note chord before returning to the low notes from the original riff. The second chorus is a repeat of the first, but with an additional single-note fill that leads into the solo.

### Bar 14 | *Fingering options*

This lead fill can, theoretically, be played using any finger. Although the first finger may appear to be the most obvious choice, using the fourth finger will leave your hand perfectly in position to use the ubiquitous A minor pentatonic shape for the solo.

## Guitar Solo (Bars 15–18)

The accompaniment for the guitar solo is based on the chorus chords. Create your own solo for this section.

### Bars 15–18 | *Scale choices*

The solo section is in the key of A minor, so the most obvious scale choices are the A minor pentatonic and A natural minor scales.

## Bridge (Bars 19–26)

The bridge starts with a subdued variation of the main riff. The second half of the section features accented chords followed by melodies played using natural harmonics.

### Bars 19–22 | *Volume adjustments*

The notes in the bridge riff must be allowed to ring into each other to obtain the correct sound. To stop this section turning into an indistinguishable mush, turn the guitar's volume control down to reduce the amount of distortion.

### Bars 23–26 | *Natural harmonics*

Natural harmonics (Fig. 2) are sounded by lightly placing your finger *directly over* the frets. Your finger placement for the 5th fret harmonics must be fairly precise, so don't be discouraged if it takes a little while to sound them correctly.

## Chorus 3 & Outro (Bars 27–38)

The final chorus is a variation of the previous two and is followed by the outro that combines powerchords and single notes to bring the arrangement to a close.

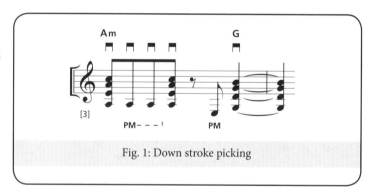

Fig. 1: Down stroke picking

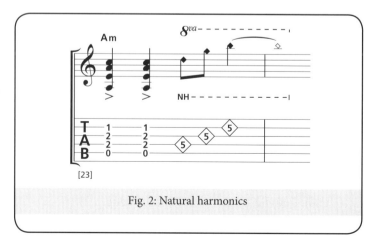

Fig. 2: Natural harmonics

SONG TITLE: CIGARETTES AND ALCOHOL
ALBUM: DEFINITELY MAYBE
RELEASED: 1994
LABEL: CREATION
GENRE: INDIE

PERSONNEL: NOEL GALLAGHER (GTR)
LIAM GALLAGHER (VOX)
PAUL ARTHURS (GTR)
PAUL MCGUIGAN (BASS)
BRETT MORGAN (DRUMS)

UK CHART PEAK: 7
US CHART PEAK: N/A

*© Peter Pakvis | Redferns*

## BACKGROUND INFO

'Cigarettes and Alcohol' was the fourth single from Oasis's 1994 debut album *Definitely Maybe*. They had achieved chart success with two previous singles, but this was their first UK top ten and was the final part of their rise to the big leagues. The song has its roots firmly in the classic British rock of the 60s and 70s and much has been made of the main riff's similarity to T-Rex's 'Get It On'.

## THE BIGGER PICTURE

When Oasis burst onto the scene in 1994, guitar playing was going through something of an 'anti guitar solo' movement. Early 90s punk and grunge dominated guitar music and lead solos were on the decline following a backlash against the self-indulgent rock music of the 80s when extended guitar solos were the norm. This eventually culminated in virtuoso instrumental albums by guitarists such as Steve Vai and Joe Satriani. Noel Gallagher's lead style struck the perfect balance between these two opposing approaches. His solos on songs like 'Supersonic' and 'Live Forever' had the excitement that makes lead guitar an important element of guitar playing, but were still melodic and memorable enough to be a integral part of the song.

## NOTES

Leading up to the release of their second album *(What's The Story) Morning Glory?*, Oasis were involved in the much-hyped 'Battle of Britpop', with Damon Alburn fronted band Blur. Both bands released singles simultaneously with Blur's 'Country House' pipping 'Roll With It' to the number one spot. Oasis took their 'revenge' when *(What's The Story) Morning Glory?* beat Blur's *The Great Escape* to the top position in the album charts a short time later.

## RECOMMENDED LISTENING

While the first part of their career might have been Oasis's most successful there's still plenty of great music contained within their later catalogue. 'Go Let It Out' from 2000's *Standing On The Shoulder Of Giants* is a typical Oasis strum-along. 'Songbird', written by Liam Gallagher is a simple two-chord progression with a catchy chorus.

The 1998 compilation *The Masterplan* shouldn't be overlooked. This collection of B-sides and discarded album tracks contains some of Oasis's best work, including the acoustic 'Talk Tonight', the swaggering, 'Acquiesce' and the epic, inexplicably previously unreleased 'The Masterplan'.

# Cigarettes & Alcohol

## Oasis

Words & Music by Noel Gallagher

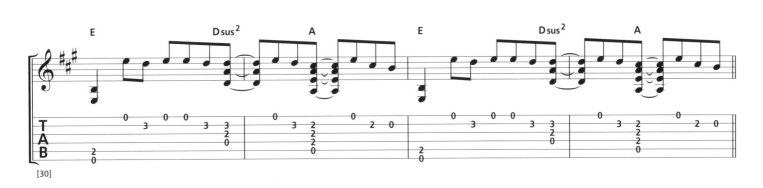

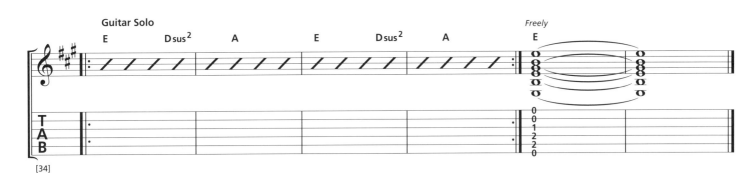

# Walkthrough

## Tone
Turn the gain up to produce a highly overdriven sound. Boost the middle and treble settings to add some edge to the guitar's tone and help it cut through the mix. Add some reverb to fill out the sound, particularly in the guitar solo.

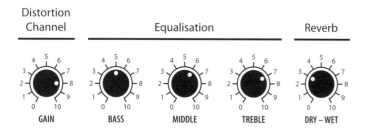

## Intro (Bars 1–12)
The arrangement starts with a solo guitar playing a rock 'n' rock-inspired low riff. After a high-register fill the guitar plays a syncopated riff that combines low notes on the sixth string with a higher, fretted chord shape.

**Bar 8** | *Quick position shifts*
Move your hand from the two-note chord at the 10th fret to the barre chord at the 9th fret while you are playing the open sixth string. This will help you perform a seamless transition from one chord to the next.

**Bars 8–12** | *Counting rhythms*
This rhythm is quite challenging, so start slowly as you learn the part. Count the bar in eighth notes ("1 & 2 & 3 & 4 &") and gradually increase the speed as you become more comfortable with the riff. Fig. 1 shows you where each note should be played in relation to the count.

## Verse (Bars 13–21)
The verse is similar to the intro with the exception of the open strings used to embellish the F♯ chord. Candidates should improvise their own rhythm part on the repeat.

**Bars 20 & 21** | *First and second time bars*
The first and second time bars in the main riff indicate the first time you reach the end of bar 19 you should play bar 20. The second time you reach the end of bar 19 you should miss out bar 20 and play bar 21.

## Chorus (Bars 22–33)
The first half of the chorus is a low-string riff that uses quarter-tone bends. The second half is a more open flowing part that uses open chords.

**Bars 22–27** | *Quarter-tone bends*
The chorus features multiple instances of quarter-tone bends (Fig. 2). Quarter-tone bends are usually a quick bend and

players should avoid wasting time trying to make them precisely a quarter tone. Use your instinct to guide you, as quarter-tone bends are a technique that rely heavily on 'feel' to obtain the right sound.

## Outro/Solo (Bars 34–39)
The guitar solo is played over the same chords as the second half of the chorus. A sustained free-time E chord brings the arrangement to a close.

**Bars 34–37** | *Guitar Solo*
While there are several scale choices for this solo section, the original version uses the E minor pentatonic scale and this is certainly the easiest option as none of its notes clash with any of the chords. You should look to create a solo that fits stylistically with the song and complements the backing.

**Bars 38–39** | *'Freely' performance direction*
Music that is in 'free time' has no regular pulse and the notes are played when the performer feels it's the right time to do so. A 'freely' performance direction, indicates that, although the music is written in bars and given note values, this should be treated as a guide and the performance should be interpreted by the performer.

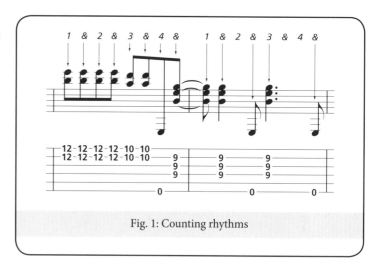

Fig. 1: Counting rhythms

Fig. 2: Quarter-tone bends

SONG TITLE: GOLDEN TOUCH
ALBUM: UP ALL NIGHT
RELEASED: 2004
LABEL: MECURY
GENRE: INDIE

PERSONNEL: JOHNNY BORRELL (GTR+VOX)
ANDY BURROWS (DRUMS)
BJÖRN ÅGREN (GUITAR)
CARL DALEMO (BASS)

UK CHART PEAK: 9
US CHART PEAK: N/A

© Janette Beckman | Premium Archive

## BACKGROUND INFO

'Golden Touch' is the fourth single from Razolight's debut album *Up All Night*. It starts with a guitar playing staccato chords with the bass guitar. The first chorus adds a second guitar playing high, arpeggiated chords. The drums finally join in the second verse and the song continues to crescendo with the addition of backing vocals and a guitar playing high, staccato chords. After reaching its peak the dynamics drop down for a mellow finale.

## THE BIGGER PICTURE

After some success with *Up All Night*, Razorlight's 2006's eponymous album took the band's status to a new level. It contains three UK top 20 singles, including the number 1 'America'. Almost constant airplay has ensured that it will be considered a classic in years to come. *Slipway Fires*, hasn't reached the same levels of success as its predecessor but Razorlight are still one of the world's premier indie acts.

## NOTES

Various acoustic versions exist of 'Golden Touch', most notably on 2006 Radio 1's 'Live Lounge' release.

The performances are often bolstered with the additional of a female choir. Fans of the song should seek this, excellent, alternative version.

## RECOMMENDED LISTENING

*Up All Night* is a raw, stripped-down affair compared to Razorlight's subsequent releases (undoubtedly due to larger recording budgets after their early success). Highlights include 'Stumble and Fall' and UK number 2 'Somewhere Else'.

The three biggest hits from *Razorlight* are also the finest on the album. 'In The Morning' features some interesting funky guitar parts, while 'Before I Fall To Pieces' makes use of the familiar Razorlight technique of combined low strummed chords with a high arpeggiated part. The famous main riff to 'America' is played using a capo and is treated with a delay effect to add to its chiming sound.

*Slipway Fires* contains some excellent acoustic moments. 'Hostage Of Love', which has a folk-influenced feel and uses high caped open chords and '60 Thompson' has a finger-picked intro that owes no small debt to folk-rock legend Richard Thompson, though there's no indication that the title is anything more than a coincidence.

# Golden Touch

## Razorlight

Words & Music by Johnny Borrell

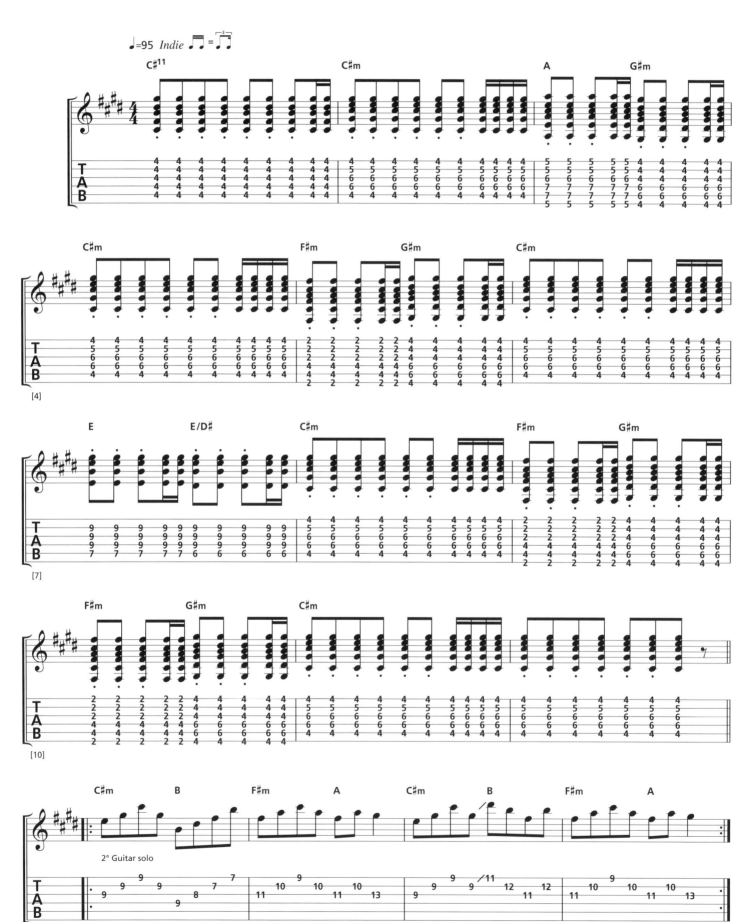

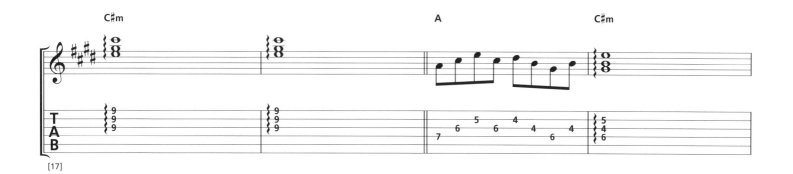

[17]

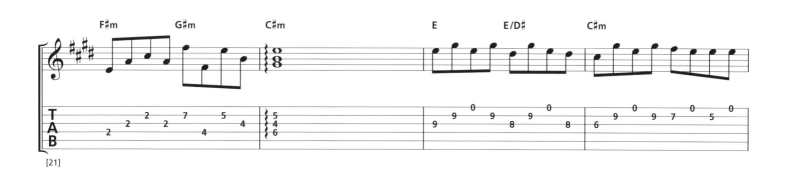

[21]

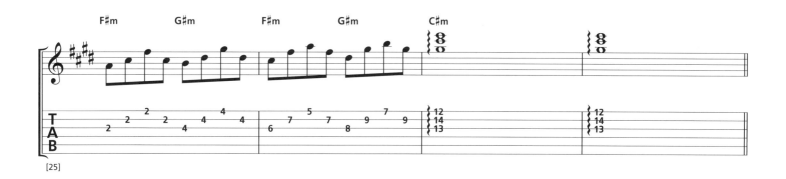

[25]

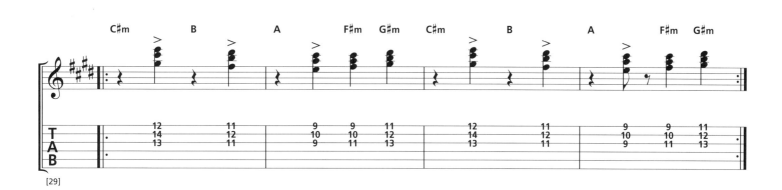

[29]

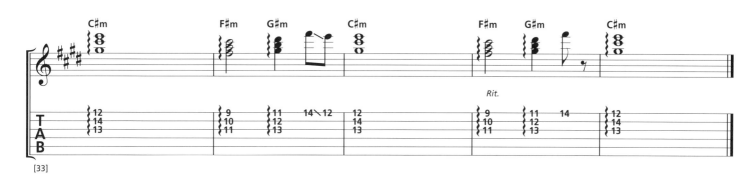

[33]

# Walkthrough

## Tone

Aim for a warm, full clean tone that isn't too thin. If you have a guitar fitted with singlecoil pickups select the neck pickup for the warmest possible sound. Adding reverb will fill out the sound somewhat, particularly on the high picked sections, but as always, be careful not to add too much and swamp the guitar.

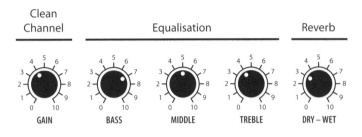

| Clean Channel | Equalisation | | | Reverb |
|---|---|---|---|---|
| GAIN | BASS | MIDDLE | TREBLE | DRY – WET |

## Intro/Verse 1 (Bars 1–12)

The intro and first verse consists of staccato barre chords played in a swung sixteenth-note rhythm.

### Bars 1–12 | *Staccato Chords*

The dots above the eighth notes in bars 1–12 (Fig. 1) indicates they should be played 'staccato' meaning 'short and detached'. To achieve this sound, release the pressure on the strings as soon as you play the note. Don't take your fingers all the way off the strings, simply stop pressing down.

### Bars 1–12 | *Sixteeth-note strumming*

To play this section fluently you will need to use sixteenth-note strumming. This is where the picking hand strums four times for every beat of the bar. The pick doesn't strike the string four times per beat: some of these will be 'ghost' strums. Sixteenth notes are counted as: "1 e & a 2 e & a 3 e & a 4 e & a".

### Bars 1–12 | *Ghost strums*

Keeping your hand in a constant strumming motion between chord hits helps to make rhythm parts more fluent. When you don't want to strike the strings move your pick a small amount away from them. These are called 'ghost strums'. Fig. 2 shows how the constant strumming motion corresponds to the rhythm of the verse.

## Chorus 1 (Bars 13–18)

The first chorus features arpeggiated chords (each note played separately). The repeat of the section is an opportunity for candidates to improvise.

### Bars 17–18 | *Spread chords*

The wavy line that runs vertically alongside the chords in bars 17 & 18 indicates that, even though the chord tones are notated to be played simultaneously, you should spread them out slightly. Rather than strumming the chord, brush your pick across the strings to produce a sound that is midway between a strummed chord and one that is arpeggiated.

### Bars 13–18 | *Improvisation*

The C♯ minor pentatonic and C♯ natural minor scales are the two most appropriate scale choices for this solo. Correct scale choices alone don't guarantee a good guitar solo, though. It's important to improvise a part that sits well against the rest of the track.

## Verse 2 (Bars 19–28)

The second verse uses combinations of arpeggiated and spread chords. Open strings are used to add colour to basic chords in the descending section of the progression.

## Chorus 2 (Bars 29–32)

The second chorus uses high-position, triads which predominately accent the weaker second and fourth beats of the bar, this is known as syncopation.

### Bars 29–32 | *Accents*

An accent sign is placed above or below a note head. When you see this sign you should accent the marked note by playing it slightly louder than the other notes in the phrase.

## Outro (Bars 33–37)

The outro consists of spread high-position triads (see above) on the top three strings, that are embellished with the occasional single note.

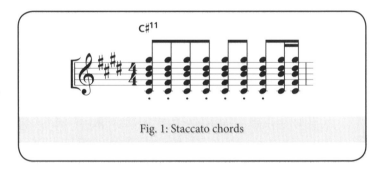

Fig. 1: Staccato chords

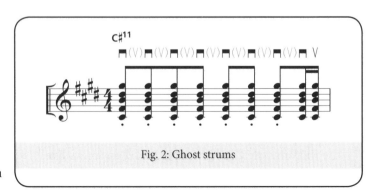

Fig. 2: Ghost strums

# Jimi Hendrix Experience

SONG TITLE: HEY JOE
ALBUM: N/A
RELEASED: 1966
LABEL: POLYDOR
GENRE: ROCK

PERSONNEL: JIMI HENDRIX (GTR+VOX)
NOEL REDDING (BASS)
MITCH MITCHELL (DRUMS)

UK CHART PEAK: 6
US CHART PEAK: N/A

© Petra Niemeier | K & K

## BACKGROUND INFO

Hendrix's version of Billy Robert's 'Hey Joe' was their first single and helped launch them in the UK. It opens with one of the most famous guitar parts in the history of rock music. The rest of the song is based on a single C–G–D–A–E progression, but this only tells half the story of the song. Using his patented rhythm style (see below) Hendrix never plays the chords the same way twice. Later in the song the progression is developed by adding a walking bassline which is doubled by the guitar.

## THE BIGGER PICTURE

Jimi Hendrix's impact on the history of the guitar is immeasurable. His innovative playing, experimentation with guitar tones and flamboyant stage moves have without question, influenced more guitarists than anyone else.

## NOTES

With so much focus on Hendrix's exceptional lead guitar work, it's all too easy to overlook his fluid rhythm style. Initially he was influenced by the rhythm style Curtis Mayfield used on tracks like

'People Get Ready' and soul legend Steve Cropper. Hendrix embellished chord fragments of two or three notes with slides, hammer-ons and pull-offs. He would often play his version of the standard six-string barre chords by playing the 'F' shape with his first, second and third fingers while playing the lowest note with his thumb (the fifth string was unplayed). This gave him the full range of the chord and freed his fourth finger for embellishment. This allowed Hendrix to bridge the gap between rhythm and lead playing and helped him avoid the monotony of simply strumming chords. This is one of the most recognisable elements of his playing and has been used subsequently by countless players since, but most notably Stevie Ray Vaughan.

## RECOMMENDED LISTENING

1967's *Are You Experienced* contains more classic tracks than most artists' entire greatest hits collections, among them: 'Foxy Lady', 'Manic Depression', 'Red House' and 'Fire'. The 1968 follow up, *Axis: Bold Of Love* is equally stacked, boasting 'Little Wing', 'If 6 was 9' and 'Spanish Castle Magic'. *Electric Ladyland* was the last release with the original lineup and contains 'Voodoo Child (Slight Return)', 'Crosstown Traffic' and their sublime cover of Bob Dylan's 'All Along The Watchtower'.

# Hey Joe

## Jimi Hendrix Experience

Words & Music by Billy Roberts

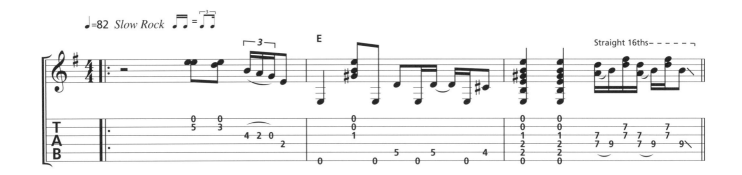

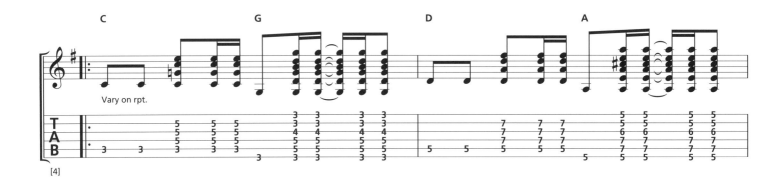

[4]

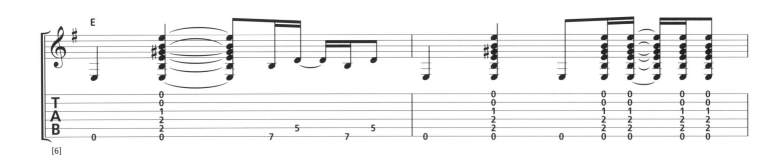

[6]

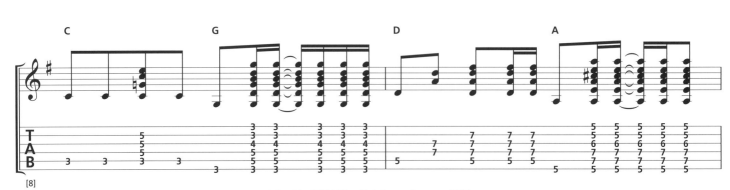

[8]

**Guitar Solo**

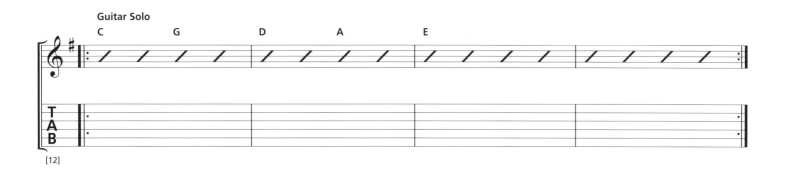

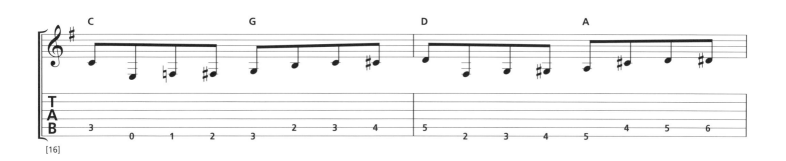

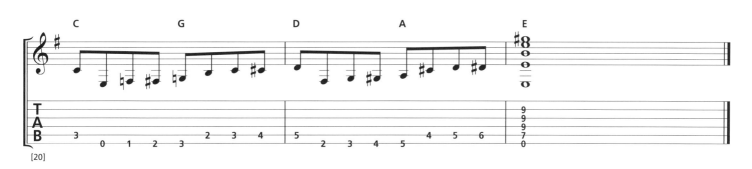

# Walkthrough

## Tone

While it's possible to play Hey Joe with a clean tone, setting the distortion channel to a low gain setting will mean the sound will break up slightly when the guitar is played more aggressively. This will help fill the sound out, particularly in the guitar solo.

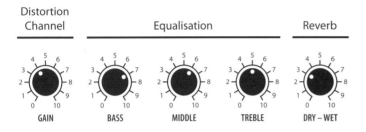

## Intro (Bars 1–3)

The intro starts with a blues-influenced open string lick that moves to a low single-note riff before finishing with a lick that combines hammer-ons and double-stops

### Bar 1 | *Sixteenth-note triplet*

On paper this rhythm looks intimidating, but performing the quick pull-off will naturally produce this rhythm. If you still feel unsure, pay close attention to the full recording to hear how the rhythm should sound.

### Bar 3 | *Double-stops with hammer-ons*

Fret the notes at the 7th fret with your first finger and then hammer-on the note at the 9th fret of the fourth string with your third finger (Fig. 1). Make sure you use the tip of your finger so that you arch over the third string to allow the notes at the 7th fret to ring clearly. This awkward movement will take some practice to master, so don't be discouraged if it takes longer than you think it should to play it correctly.

## Verse (Bars 4–11)

The verse cycles through four barre chords that use sixteenth notes and concludes with a low E chord and pentatonic fill in fifth position. Candidates should improvise their own rhythm part on the repeat.

### Bars 4–11 | *Sixteenth-note strumming*

You will need to use sixteenth-note strumming. This is where the picking hand strums four times for every beat of the bar. The pick doesn't strike the string four times per beat: some of these will be 'ghost' strums. Sixteenth notes are counted as: "1 e & a 2 e & a 3 e & a 4 e & a".

### Bars 4–11 | *Ghost strums*

Keeping your hand in a constant strumming motion between chord hits helps to make rhythm parts more fluent. When you don't want to strike the strings move your pick

a small amount away from them, these are called 'ghost strums'. Fig. 2 shows how the constant strumming motion corresponds to the rhythm of the verse. The ghost strums are also indicated.

### Bars 4–11 | *Improvised accompaniment*

You should create your own rhythm part for these 8 bars. Avoid trying to cram too much into your playing: you should look to improvise a part that fits stylistically with the rest of the piece.

## Solo (Bars 12–15)

The progression the guitar solo is to be played over is the same as the verse.

### Bars 12–15 | *Guitar Solo*

While there are several scale choices for this solo section the original version uses the E minor pentatonic scale and this is certainly the easiest option as none of its notes clash with any of the chords in the backing track. You should look to create a solo that fits stylistically with the song and complements the backing.

## Outro (Bars 16–22)

The outro uses the same chord progression as the rest of the song, but the guitar plays a 'walking' riff that doubles the bass guitar parts.

Fig. 1: Double-stops with hammer-ons

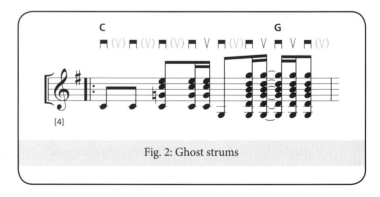

Fig. 2: Ghost strums

SONG TITLE: PARANOID
ALBUM: PARANOID
RELEASED: 1970
LABEL: VERTIGO
GENRE: HEAVY METAL

PERSONNEL: OZZY OSBOURNE (VOX)
TONY IOMMI (GTR)
GEEZER BUTLER (BASS)
BILL WARD (DRUMS)

UK CHART PEAK: 4
US CHART PEAK: 61

*© Steve Emberton | Hulton Archive*

## BACKGROUND INFO

'Paranoid' was the first single from the 1970 album of the same name. It starts with a distinctive guitar riff based on an $E^5$ powerchord and the minor pentatonic scale before moving into chugging eighth-note powechords for the majority of the song. The interesting guitar tone in the solo is the sound of a ring modulator effect. It may be simple, but 'Paranoid' netted Black Sabbath their highest ever chart position and initiated their rise to superstardom.

## THE BIGGER PICTURE

Black Sabbath's sound evolved from the blues to the powerful sound that became the blueprint of today's modern metal. Megadeth and Metallica constantly reference Black Sabbath as an influence, while Alice in Chains and Soundgarden clearly owe a debt to them. Grunge icon, Kurt Cobain name-checked Sabbath when describing Nirvana's sound.

## NOTES

'Paranoid' was written as an album filler (its relatively simple structure compared to the rest of the album supports this). In fact, the album *Paranoid* was supposed to be named after another track on the album: 'War Pigs'. The title was changed by the record company as it was considered inappropriate in light of the ongoing Vietnam war. This is why the figure on the front cover of the album is clearly a 'War Pig'.

One interesting quirk of guitarist Tony Iommi's style is that he prefers to play powerchords on the lowest two strings of the guitar (the fifth and sixth strings) regardless of how high they are. This means he often plays above the 12th fret, even when it might seem more logical to play one string higher. This approach yields a thick, full tone that can't be duplicated on the thinner strings.

## RECOMMENDED LISTENING

'Evil Woman' from Sabbath's debut album *Black Sabbath* shows off Iommi's Clapton-influenced lead style. The title track, is perhaps the first recorded example of the heavy metal genre. It makes use of the dark sounding tritone ($\flat5$) interval combined with a heavy, distorted sound, which, while commonplace in metal nowadays, was groundbreaking in the late 60s. Some of Tony Iommi's best riffs can be found on 1973's *Sabbath Bloody Sabbath*. Aside from the title track, 'A National Acrobat' features an excellent harmony riff and 'Sabbra Cadabra' harks back to Sabbath's bluesy beginnings.

## Black Sabbath

Words & Music by Ozzy Osbourne, Tony Iommi, Terry 'Geezer' Butler & Bill Ward

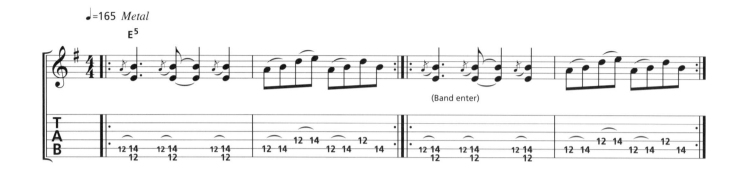

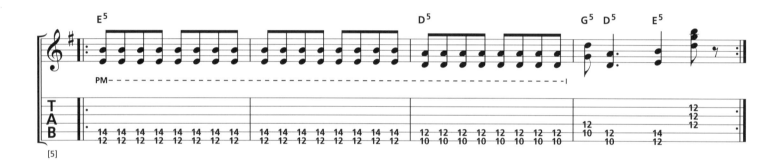

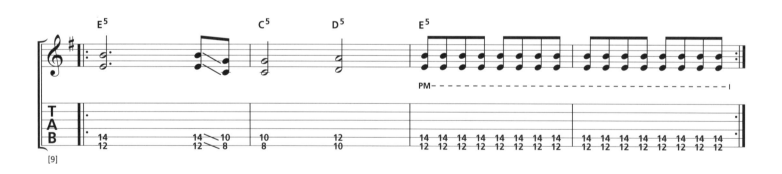

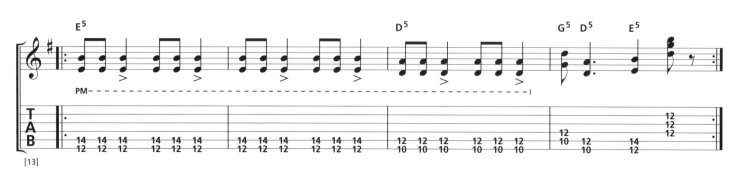

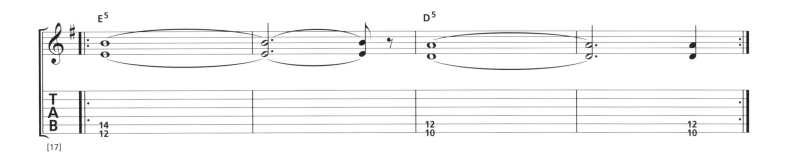

[17]

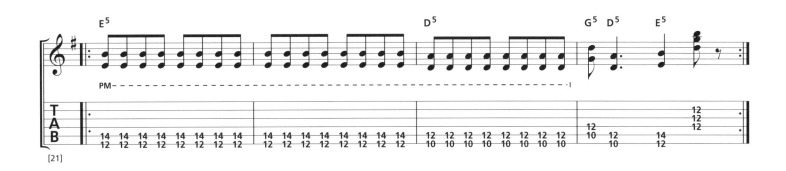

[21]

**Guitar Solo**

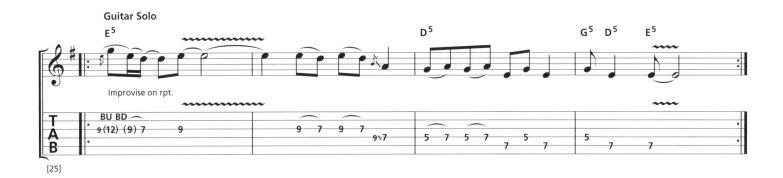

Improvise on rpt.

[25]

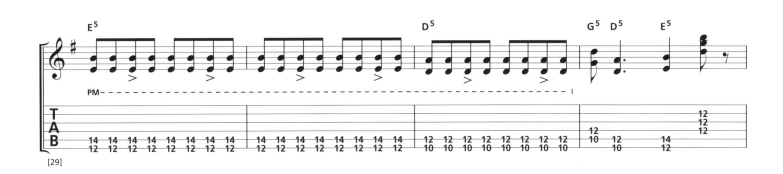

[29]

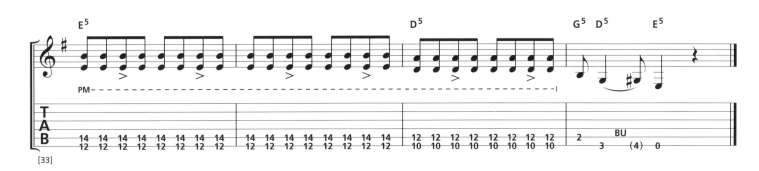

[33]

# Walkthrough

## Tone

Although Black Sabbath shaped the modern metal guitar tone, they didn't have access to the hi-gain sounds available now. For an authentic sound, opt for a heavily overdriven sound and boost the bass and treble a little.

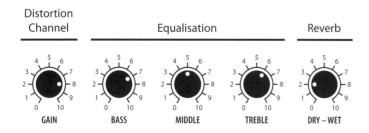

## Intro (Bars 1–4)

The arrangement begins with a solo guitar riff that uses a powerchord embellished with a grace note hammer-on. This is followed by a one-bar E minor pentatonic phrase. The band joins in after the repeat and the riff is repeated.

### Bars 1–4 | *Grace notes*

Grace notes have no timing value of their own, and are played as quickly as possible without interrupting the rhythm or flow of the music. They are represented in the tab by slightly smaller numbers than 'normal' notes. Use the first finger to form a partial barre across the 12th fret and hammer-on with the third finger.

## Verse 1 (Bars 5–16)

The verse riffs are based almost exclusively on two-note powerchords played in an eighth-note rhythm. The arrangement introduces accents and slight changes in the rhythm to vary the parts.

### Bars 5–7 | *Fast down-picking*

To achieve a consistent sound, it's best to play these powerchords with downstrokes. The high tempo makes this quite demanding. Start slowly using a metronome to help you keep time and concentrate on minimising motion from your picking hand. The pick should only travel a small amount past the fifth string and return to just above the sixth string ready for the next strike of the chord.

### Bar 8 | *Quick powerchord changes*

Rather than think about placing your fingers on individual notes within a chord, lock your hand and fingers in the powerchord 'shape' and move your hand as a unit rather than as individual fingers.

### Bars 13–15 | *Accents*

An accent sign is placed above or below a note head (Fig. 1). When you see this sign you should accent the marked note by playing it slightly louder.

## Bridge (Bars 17–24)

The bridge section consists solely of two long, sustained, two-note powerchords followed by a reprise of the first riff found in the verse.

## Guitar Solo (Bars 25–28)

The first four bars are heavily based on the original solo. The second half of the solo is an opportunity for the candidate to improvise their own solo.

### Bar 25 | *Minor 3rd bend*

A minor 3rd bend, where the pitch of a note is raised by three frets (Fig. 2), is physically demanding and will take some strength to play correctly. Perform it with the first finger assisted by the first and second fingers placed behind it. Some players hook their thumb over the top of the neck for extra leverage.

### Bars 25–28 | *Improvised solo*

The E minor pentatonic and E natural minor scales are the most obvious scale choices to improvise over this progression. Aim to create a solo that is in keeping with the style of the piece.

## Verse 2/Outro (29–36)

The outro is the same as the first riff in the verse, but ends with a low E minor pentatonic fill that brings the arrangement to a close.

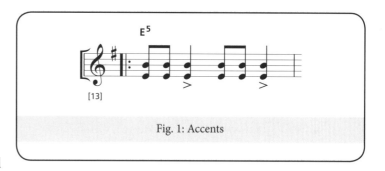

Fig. 1: Accents

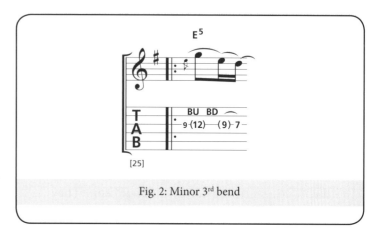

Fig. 2: Minor 3rd bend

SONG TITLE: SEX ON FIRE
ALBUM: ONLY BY THE NIGHT
RELEASED: 2008
LABEL: RCA
GENRE: ROCK

PERSONNEL: CALEB FOLLOWILL (GTR+VOX)
MATTHEW FOLLOWILL (GTR)
NATHAN FOLLOWILL (DRUMS)
JARED FOLLOWILL (BASS)

UK CHART PEAK: 1
US CHART PEAK: 56

© Jason Sheldon | Redferns

## BACKGROUND INFO

'Sex On Fire' was the first single from Kings of Leon's fourth album, the multi-platinum *Only By The Night*. It achieved the number 1 spot in the UK singles chart and is one of the most downloaded tracks in the UK. The song's syncopated main riff drives the song along and the chorus features a distinctive lead guitar part that uses open strings and unison bends.

## THE BIGGER PICTURE

The band consists of three brothers, Caleb, Jared and Nathan Followill. The lineup is completed by their cousin Matthew Followill. The band name is inspired by the three Followill brothers' father Ivan Leon Followill.

## NOTES

Kings Of Leon made a radical change in their direction when they recorded *Only By The Night*. As singer and guitarist Caleb Followill explained in interview, 'We knew this record was definitely gonna be our bold attempt at trying to make a record that wasn't necessarily obviously Kings of Leon'. They opted not to use producer Ethan Johns (who had produced the previous three albums) and worked to create more 'produced', melodic songs.

## RECOMMENDED LISTENING

Kings Of Leon's debut album *Youth and Young Manhood* (2003) has a raw, 'band in a room' vibe, a far cry from their relatively slick, though no less impressive, recent efforts. 'Molly's Chambers' has a simple and instantly recognisable riff. 'Happy Alone' is a driving track with excellent interplay between a guitar playing single note riffs in dropped 'D' tuning and a second guitar playing higher, jangly chords. *Aha Shake Heartbreak* (2004) saw the band moving away from their southern-rock roots towards a more commercial sound. The singles, 'King Of The Rodeo', 'Four Kicks' and 'The Bucket' are all highlights.

Aside from 'Sex On Fire', *Only By The Night* features the mega-hit 'Use Somebody'. The track switches effortlessly between sparse verses and epic wall of sound choruses. It also features an excellent melodic solo. 2010's *Down Around Sundown* sees The Kings Of Leon continuing to develop their 'new', mature sound. The single 'Radioactive' is built on a high-position guitar riff. 'Back Down South' features some excellent slide guitar work.

# Sex On Fire

## Kings of Leon

Words & Music by Caleb Followill, Nathan Followill, Jared Followill & Matthew Followill

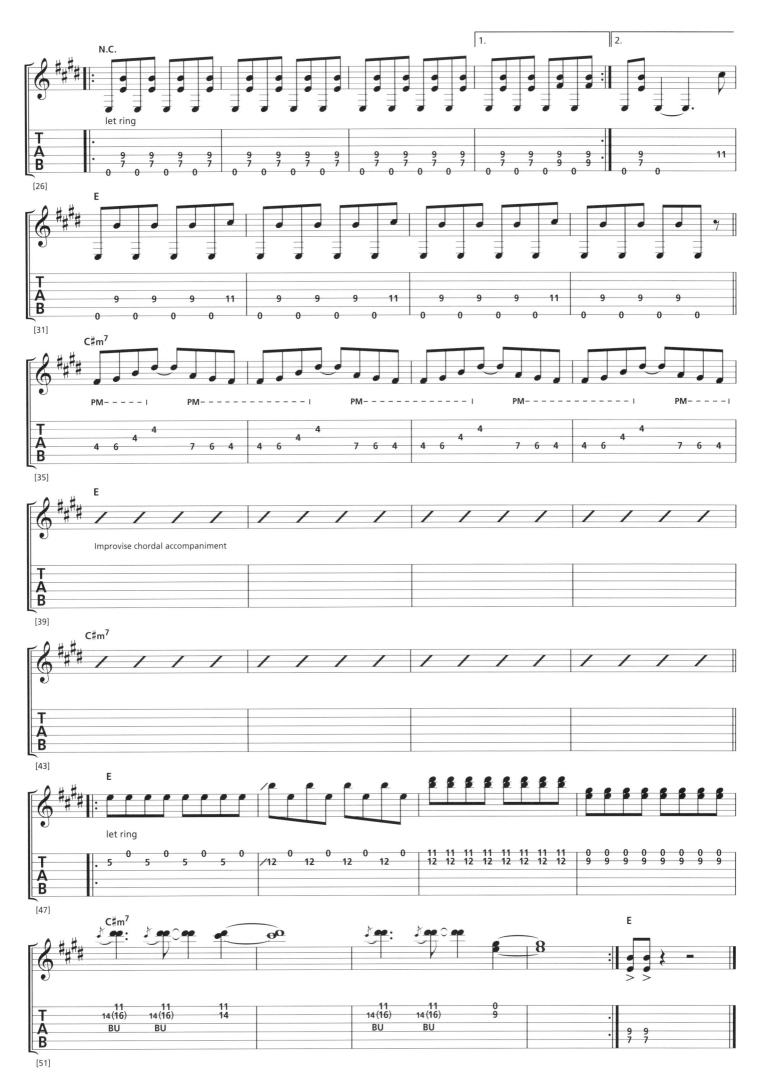

# Walkthrough

## Tone

Aim for a lightly overdriven sound that starts to distort when the guitar is played strongly. Boost the bass and cut the treble to give the sound a little more warmth. Add a little reverb, but be careful not to add too much as this will affect the guitar tone's clarity.

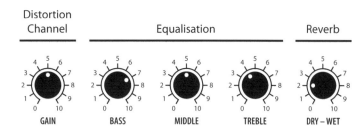

## Intro/Main riff (Bars 1–9)

The song's single-note syncopated main riff uses low pedal notes combined with fretted notes in the 9th position.

### Bars 1–5 | *Syncopation*

The main riff starts on the downbeat of beat four but accents the upbeats throughout. This is a tricky riff to play and may take some time to master, so start slowly and count along to the part as you play (Fig. 1).

## Verse 1 (Bars 10–25)

The verse starts with an arrangement of the original version's syncopated chords and the reverts to the song's main riff.

### Bars 10–17 | *Staccato chords*

The dots above the eighth notes in bars 10–17 indicates they should be played 'staccato' meaning 'short and detached'. To achieve this sound, release the pressure on the strings as soon as you play the note. Don't take your fingers all the way off the strings as this may cause unwanted noise.

## Chorus 1 (Bars 26–30)

The first chorus is a low, syncopated chordal riff that uses two-note chords and a low sixth string pedal note.

### Bars 26–29 | *Let ring*

All the notes in this section are eighth notes, but the 'let ring' direction indicates that they should be allowed to ring into each other to create a fluent, flowing part.

## Verse 2 (Bars 26–46)

The second verse starts with a reprise of the main riff then moves to a palm-muted single note riff. The final part of this section is an opportunity for the candidate to improvise a chordal accompaniment.

### Bars 39–46 | *Improvised accompaniment*

You should create your own rhythm part for these 8 bars. Avoid trying to cram too much into your playing: you should look to improvise a part that fits stylistically with the rest of the piece.

## Chorus 2 (Bars 47–55)

The second chorus starts with a part that combines open strings with fretted notes and then moves to unison bends. The arrangement finishes with two accented $E^5$ chords.

### Bars 47–50 | *Accurate fretting*

Arch your fingers to play the notes on the second string with the tip of your finger to stop the underside of the finger touching the first string, this will allow the open string to ring freely throughout the riff.

### Bars 51–54 | *Unison Bends*

A unison bend (Fig. 2) is where one note is fretted normally and a note on the next lowest string is simultaneously bent until it reaches the pitch of the un-bent note. If you have a floating bridge the two notes will never sound exactly in tune as bending the note up causes the floating bridge to raise slightly which will cause the un-bent note's pitch to drop, so the two pitches will never meet.

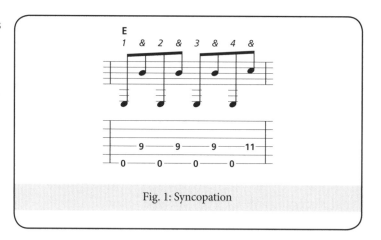

Fig. 1: Syncopation

Fig. 2: Unison bends

SONG TITLE: STEADY, AS SHE GOES
ALBUM: BROKEN BOY SOLDIERS
RELEASED: 2006
LABEL: THIRD MAN RECORDS
GENRE: ROCK

PERSONNEL: JACK WHITE (GTR+VOX)
BRENDAN BENSON (GTR+VOX)
JACK LAWRENCE (BASS)
PATRICK KEELER (DRUMS)

UK CHART PEAK: 4
US CHART PEAK: 54

© Stephane De Sakutin | AFP

## BACKGROUND INFO

'Steady, As She Goes' was the Raconteurs first single and was released just before their first album *Broken Boy Soldiers*. The song starts with a drum intro before being joined by a single-note guitar melody. The rest of the intro and verses consist of sparse, syncopated choppy guitar parts which are augmented later in the song by rhythmic muted strings. The chorus moves to a more aggressive strumming pattern that provides a perfect contrast to the more laid-back verses. The bridge section features some interesting overlapping between several voices and guitars using vintage fuzz tones. This section gradually gathers momentum as it moves towards the outro where the song builds to a rousing climax.

## THE BIGGER PICTURE

Singer and guitarist Jack White is more famous for his work as part of the blues-rock duo The White Stripes. He wrote 'Steady, As She Goes' with Brendan Benson and they decided to put a band together later adding the rhythm section of Jack Lawrence and Patrick Keeler. They described themselves as, 'a new band of old friends'. *Broken Boy Soldiers* was recorded in Benson's attic. The homemade approach was ditched for the recording of their second album.

## NOTES

The Raconteurs are known as 'The Saboteurs' in Australia. There is already a jazz band called the Raconteurs in existence. Apparently, band representatives approached the Australian Raconteurs and offered, 'a paltry sum of cash' which they turned down on 'artistic levels'.

## RECOMMENDED LISTENING

*Broken Boy Soldiers* is an impressive debut and includes the upbeat acoustic 'Yellow Sun', the Beatles influenced 'Hands' and the quirky 'Broken Boy Soldier' which features slide guitar, driving rhythms and White's tortured vocal. 2008's *Consolers Of The Lonely* continued the stripped down, eclectic, retro vibe of its predecessor, but is even more stylistically diverse. 'Many Shades Of Black' has an interesting 6/8 groove, 60s chord progression and even features a brass section in the chorus.

Although White insists the Raconteurs is a band in their own right, it's impossible to ignore The White Stripes' exceptional output. 'Seven Nation Army' from 2003's *Elephant* is so famous it's become a crowd chant at sports matches. The stripped down, 'Ball and Biscuit' shows off White's authentic blues feel.

# Steady, As She Goes

## The Raconteurs

Words & Music by Jack White & Brendan Benson

# Walkthrough

## Tone

Jack White is famous for his love of vintage equipment, so you should aim for a fairly overdriven sound. Boost the middle and treble to help the guitar cut through the rest of the track and provide some bite to your guitar's tone.

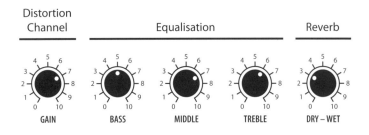

## Intro (Bars 1–8)

The first four bars of the intro consists of a single-note melody with vibrato applied to each note. The second four bars sees the guitar part playing a syncopated, staccato rhythm using a combination of open and barre chords

### Bars 1–4 | *Vibrato*

Vibrato varies tremendously from one player to another: it is one of the most distinctive aspects of a guitarist's style. Whether your vibrato is fast and wide or slow and shallow, make sure that the movement it is even and consistent otherwise your playing will sound out of tune.

### Bars 5–9 | *Correct note values*

This part's effectiveness relies on the chords lasting for only the notated length. To achieve this, release the pressure on the strings as soon as you play the note. Don't take your fingers all the way off the strings, simply stop pressing down.

## Verse 1 & Chorus 1 (Bars 9–18)

The verse uses the same progression as the second half of the intro, but delays the second chord hit by a single eighth note. The chorus uses the same progression as the intro and verse, but, in contrast, the rhythm is much more flowing and open.

### Bars 15–18 | *Incidental open strings*

The last eighth-note of every bar in this, and the bridge section, are three open strings (Fig. 1). These are an incidental sound that shouldn't be copied slavishly. They sound because the fretting fingers are moving to the next chord and aren't fretting any notes but the strumming hand is still moving in an eighth-note rhythm.

## Verse 2 & Chorus 2 (Bars 19–30)

The second verse is a reprise of the first and is an opportunity for the candidate to improvise their own rhythm part. The second chorus is a reprise of the first.

### Bars 19–26 | *Improvised accompaniment*

You should create your own rhythm part for these 8 bars. Avoid trying to cram too much into your playing: you should look to improvise a part that fits stylistically with the rest of the piece.

## Bridge & Interlude (Bars 31–54)

The bridge uses barre chords and is rhythmically similar to the chorus. The interlude is a single guitar arrangement of the original version's multiple guitar parts. It is a single-note call and response section that jumps registers frequently.

### Bars 43–50 | *Position shifts*

There are at least two beats' rest between each position shift (Fig. 2). Avoid the temptation to let the last note of each phrase ring on beyond its notated value. You should use this time to move your hand swiftly to the new position, rather than waiting until just before it's time to play the notes before moving.

## Outro (Bars 55–60)

The outro is a single guitar arrangement of the multiple guitar parts found on the original version. It moves between strummed barre chords and single-note riff.

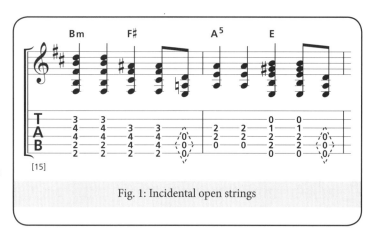

Fig. 1: Incidental open strings

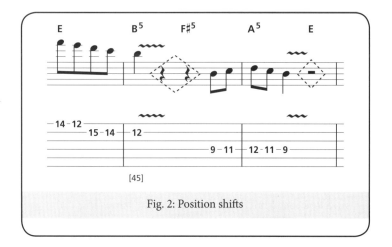

Fig. 2: Position shifts

# Wherever I May Roam

```
       SONG TITLE:  WHEREVER I MAY ROAM
           ALBUM:  METALLICA
        RELEASED:  1991
           LABEL:  ELEKTRA
           GENRE:  METAL


       PERSONNEL:  JAMES HETFIELD (GTR+VOX)
                   KIRK HAMMETT (GTR)
                   JASON NEWSTED (BASS)
                   LARS ULRICH (DRUMS)


UK CHART PEAK:  25
US CHART PEAK:  82
```

© Marty Temme | WireImage

## BACKGROUND INFO

'Wherever I May Roam' is the fifth single from Metallica's self-titled fifth album, now commonly known as the *Black Album* (the cover art is an black cover save for the faint band logo and outline of a snake). It is an epic track lasting almost seven minutes that moves between relatively subdued half-time sections and all out distorted metal riffing.

The main riff is based on the E phrygian mode (E F G A B C D E), which is the same as the E natural minor scale (E F♯ G A B C D E) except that the 2nd degree of the scale is flattened (lowered by a semitone). This mode is popular in heavy metal and hip-hop and gives the riff a dark, exotic quality.

## THE BIGGER PICTURE

Metallica are one of the most influential metal bands of all time. Many modern metal outfits are influenced by James Hefield's aggressive and extremely accurate rhythm playing. Trivium guitarists Matt Heafy and Corey Beaulieu regularly cite Hetfield and Metallica as an influence. Their third album, 2006's *Crusade,* is clearly influenced by *Master Of Puppets*. Bullet For My Valentine's rhythm guitarist and vocalist Matt Tuck has said many times in interview, that when he was younger he 'wanted to be James Hetfield' and the band's influence can be heard all through BFMV's releases, particualrly in their more recent material.

## NOTES

Kirk Hammett's solo uses a wah wah pedal. This effect features heavily in his lead work throughout the *Black Album*, particularly 'Enter Sandman' (see Hot Rock Guitar Grade 2) and 'Holier Than Thou'. The vocal-type sound that the Wah provides fitted perfectly with Hammett's move to a more melodic soloing style. Hammett told *Guitar World* magazine that producer, Bob Rock took to hiding his wah pedal through the recording of the *Black Album*.

## RECOMMENDED LISTENING

After 2003's *St Anger* was considered, by almost all concerned, to be something of a disaster the band took 5 years off and returned to action, and form, with 2008's *Death Magnetic,* which saw the band's sound harking back to the glory days of *Ride The Lightning* (1984). Highlights include 'The Day That Never Comes', 'All Nightmare Long' and 'Cyanide'.

# Wherever I May Roam

**Metallica**

Words & Music by James Hetfield & Lars Ulrich

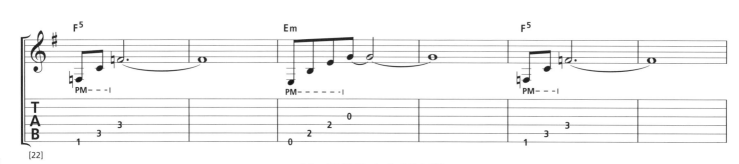

# Walkthrough

## Tone

The metal guitar tone consists of two key elements: a modern hi-gain distortion and a 'scooped' tone. A scooped tone is achieved by boosting the treble and bass controls and cutting or 'scooping out' the middle. When combined with the extreme distortion this creates a heavy, aggressive tone. Metal rhythm guitar parts like this rarely use reverb as this reduces the clarity of the genre's precise riffing style.

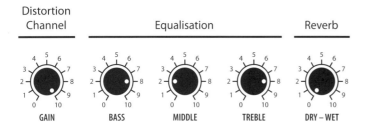

## Intro (Bars 1–9)

The intro consists of an exotic single-note riff that uses the open sixth string combined with higher fretted notes embellished with hammer-ons and slides.

**Bar 8** | *2/4 bar*
While there's nothing too complicated about a 2/4 bar inserted in the middle of a song that's predominately 4/4, it's advisable to count through the bars so you don't lose track of the strong beats on the bar.

**Bar 15** | *Fingerings*
The first four notes of the bar should be payed using the first, second, third and fourth fingers respectively. As you play the F note at the 8th fret with the fourth finger move the first finger onto the 7th fret ready to play the second half of the bar. This shift means your strongest fingers are now in position to articulate the hammer-on.

## Main riff (Bars 10–19)

The song increases tempo here and a variation of the intro riff is introduced. The basic riff is embellished with chromatic fills and finishes with a bar of 2/4.

## Verse (Bars 19–43)

The verse starts by using either sustained or palm-muted arpeggiated chords. The next section of the arrangement is based on the original version's bassline and features rhythmic, palm-muted powerchords. It finishes with two bars of an arpeggiated Eminor chord. The rest of the chord sequence is left for the candidate to improvise.

**Bars 20–44** | *Half time feel*
A half time feel gives the illusion that the song's tempo has halved. This effect is usually created by the drum pattern.

Instead of playing the bass drum on beats 1 and 3 and the snare on beats 2 and 4, plays the bass drum on beat 1 and the snare on beat 3 (Fig. 1).

**Bars 38–34** | *Improvised accompaniment*
You should create your own rhythm part for these 6 bars. Avoid trying to cram too much into your playing: you should look to improvise a part that fits stylistically with the rest of the piece.

## Chorus (Bars 44–58)

The chorus powerchords are heavily palm-muted and contrast the single note trills that give this riff an exotic sound. The chorus finishes with sustained powerchords.

**Bar 50–54** | *Trills*
Trills are indicated by the sign above the notation (Fig. 2). When you see this you should rapidly alternate between the two notes shown in brackets. In this case the trill is articulated with hammer-ons and pull-offs.

**Bars 49–54** | *Heavy palm muting*
Place the edge of the right side of your palm on the lowest-sounding strings and press firmly to get the heavy choke required for this part.

## Outro (Bars 59–64)

The outro is a reprise of the main riff and brings the arrangement to a close.

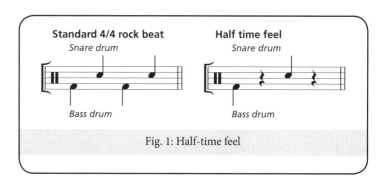

Fig. 1: Half-time feel

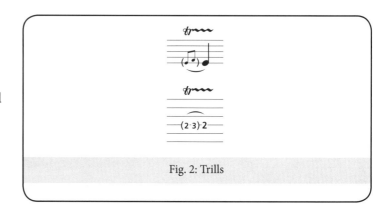

Fig. 2: Trills

# Full Transcriptions

This section contains the full transcriptions of the pieces. These have been prepared for players who would like to perform them in public examinations or for their own sake.

Further advice and tips on how to play the pieces in this form, whether for examination purposes or not, are found in the 'Notes to the Full Transcription'. This is divided into three sections: Foundation (covering Grades 1–3), Intermediate (Grades 4 and 5) and Advanced (Grades 6–8). The weighting of the advice will vary from song to song depending on the difficulty of the song in question.

Some of these songs contain very challenging elements, especially in the guitar solos. This does not mean that the whole song is automatically 'off limits' to less experienced players. In every song there is at least one section which can be played by guitarists of all abilities.

The accompanying audio for these arrangements can be found on CD2. There are two tracks for each song: the first is the full performance including the guitar part, while the second is the backing track without the main guitar part. Where parts are doubled-tracked on the original recording (different guitars playing identical parts) both parts have been removed to avoid confusion and make room for the part being performed by the candidate.

*© David Redfern | Redferns*

# Ain't Talkin' 'Bout Love

## Van Halen

Words & Music by David Lee Roth, Edward Van Halen, Alex Van Halen & Michael Anthony

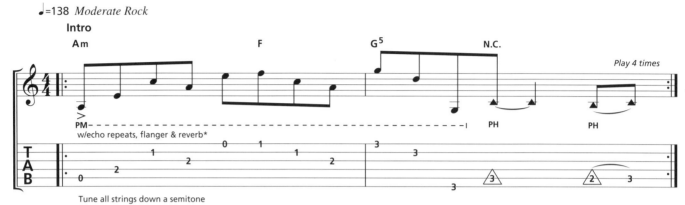

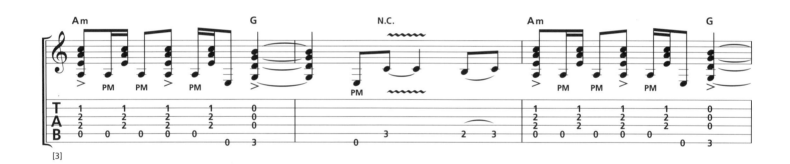

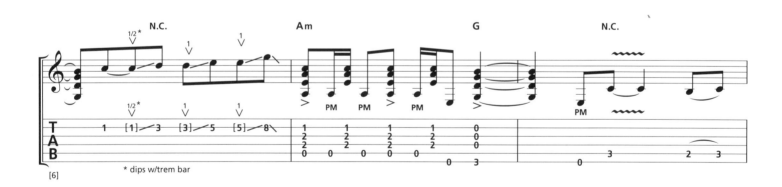

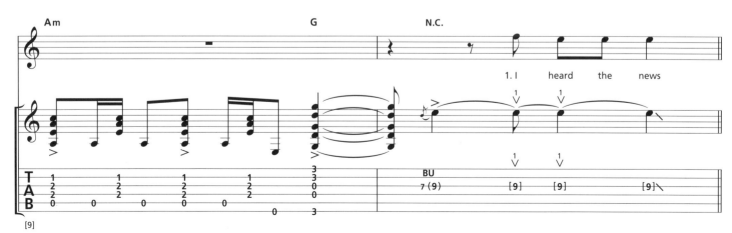

core._____                    Ain't talk-in' 'bout love.

[21]

1.

Just like I told you be-fore,_____                    yeah, be-fore._____ 2. You know you're se-mi good-

[24]

2.

Just like I told you be-fore,_____    be-fore,_____ uh, be-fore,_____ uh, be-fore,_____    be-fore.

[27]        * Hold bend while sliding                                    *Doubled by elec. sitar (Gtr. 2)

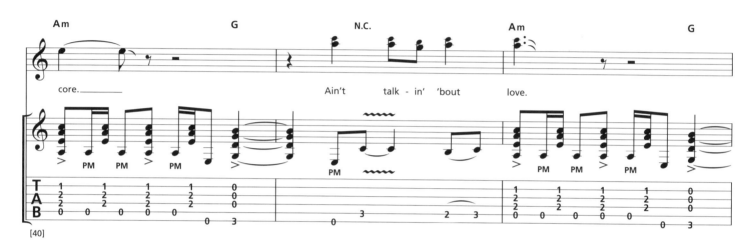

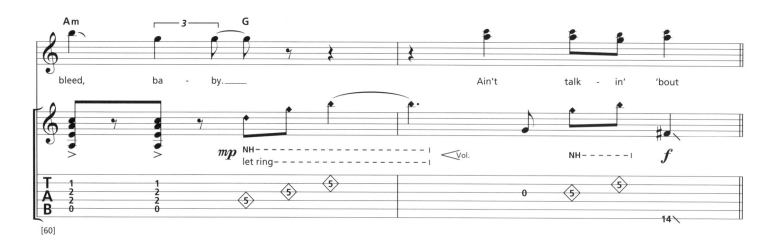

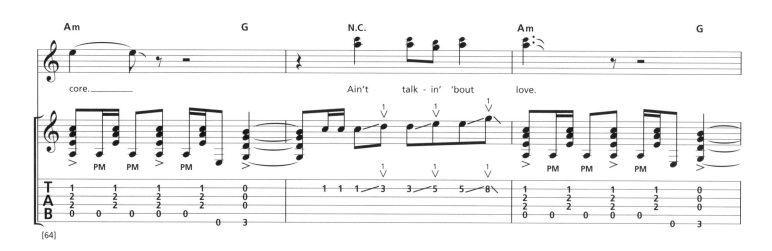

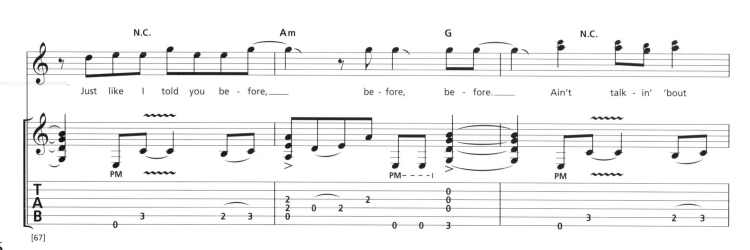

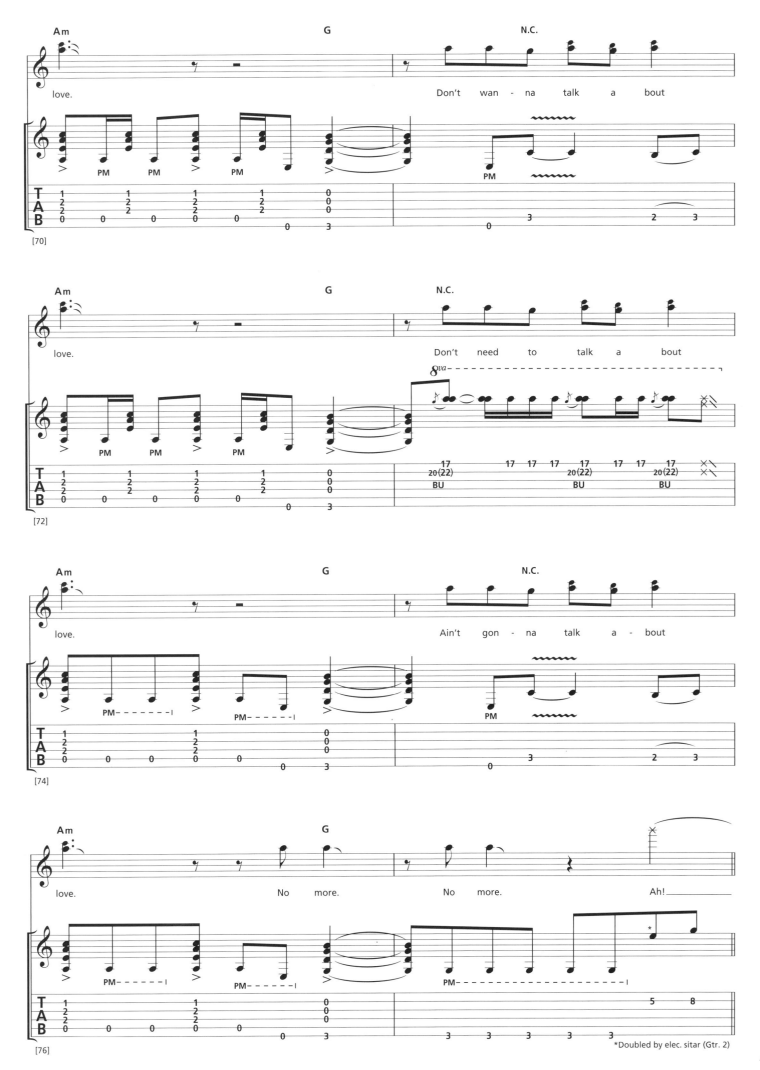

*Doubled by elec. sitar (Gtr. 2)

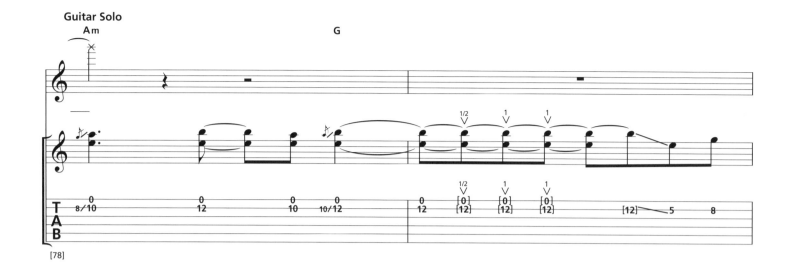

[78]

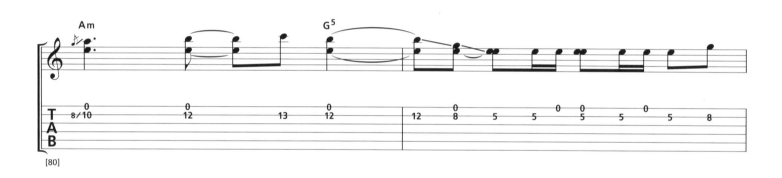

[80]

[82]

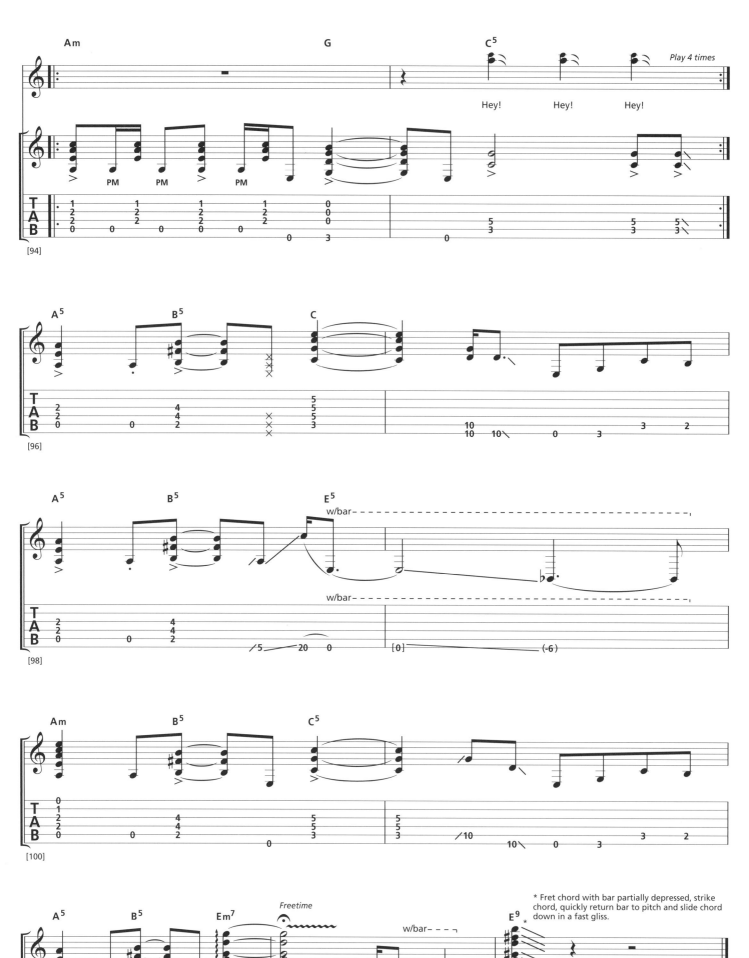

# Notes On The Full Transcription

**Note:** guitarists without a locking tremolo system will have to adapt some of the some of the parts to suit their guitar.

## Foundation Players
Players of this level will be able to play the song's main riff, but may find the rest of the parts beyond their abilities. Guitarists looking for a full arrangement to perform may find the exam version a more worthwhile study piece.

### Bar 1–104 | E♭ tuning
In the original version of this song all the guitars are tuning one semi-tone lower than standard pitch. This can also be referred to as 'E♭ tuning' or 'tuning down a half-step'. To play along to the CD you will need to re-tune your guitar, low to high, to: E♭ A♭ D♭ G♭ B♭ E♭. The notation is written as if the guitar is in standard tuning. If you don't want to play to the backing track you don't have to re-tune the guitar

### Bars 1–8 | *Palm muting*
Place the edge of the right side of your palm on the lowest sounding strings to lightly mute the strings. Be careful not to move your hand too far from the bridge as this may raise the pitch of the note. Take extra care if your guitar has a floating bridge because pressing too hard will push the bridge down and raise the pitch of the notes.

### Bars 3–10 | *Accents*
An accent sign is placed above or below a note head. There are five different kinds of accent sign, but by far the most common is the one used in this piece (Fig. 1). When you see this sign you should accent the marked note by playing it slightly louder than the other notes in the phrase.

## Intermediate Players
This is a good song for intermediate players. The guitar solos and fills will make excellent long-term studies in advanced rock guitar playing.

### Bar 14 | *Pinched Harmonics*
If you haven't tried pinched harmonics before, select your bridge pickup and use a high distortion setting to help you. Place your thumb close to the edge of the pick and dig into the strings. Both the pick and your thumb should strike the string. Pinch harmonics will only sound at certain 'node' points along the strings, so you'll need to experiment with your picking hand position.

### Bars 30–34 | *Accurate fretting*
Arch your fingers to play the notes on the second string with the tip of your finger to stop the underside of the finger touching the first string, this will allow the open string to ring freely throughout the riff.

### Bars 103–104 | *'Free time' performance direction*
A 'free time' performance direction indicates that, although the music is written in bars and has given note values, it should be treated as a guide and the performance should be interpreted by the performer. Free time sections are most often found at the beginning or end of a piece.

## Advanced Players
This is an excellent song for players of this level to learn. The high tempo and advanced techniques make this a real challenge to perform at a professional standard.

### Bar 6 | *Whammy bar dips*
These dips are very rhythmic and are performed by bouncing the bar in time with the music (Fig. 2). As mentioned in the previous step, only small movements are required to hit the correct pitches.

### Bar 37 | *Whammy bar dives*
The whammy bar dives throughout the track are wild and flamboyant and add a high level of excitement. Slight movements of the bar will alter a note's pitch by a surprising amount, so even extreme dives, like those found in 'Aint Talkin' 'Bout Love', require small, controlled movements. Depress the bar slowly and evenly to get the correct sound.

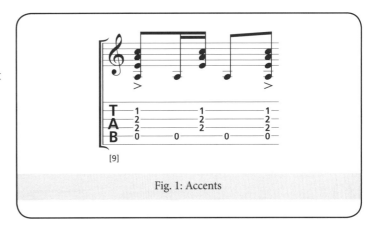

Fig. 1: Accents

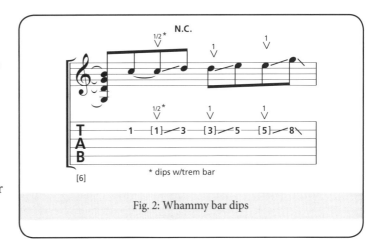

Fig. 2: Whammy bar dips

# Cigarettes & Alcohol

## Oasis

Words & Music by Noel Gallagher

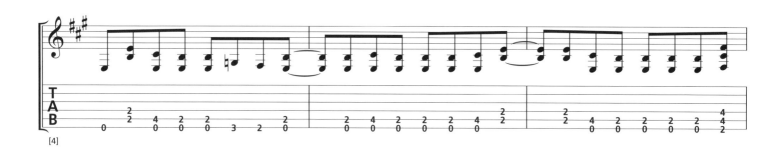

[4]

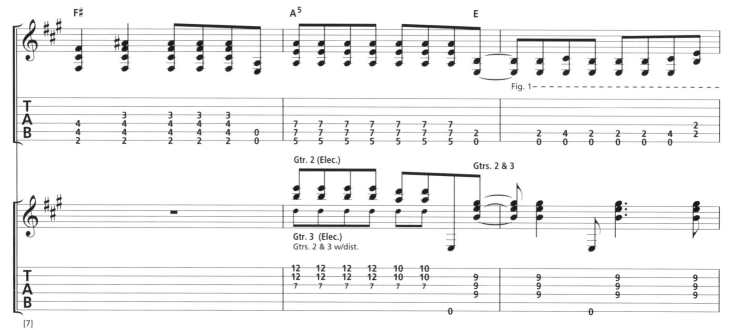

[7]

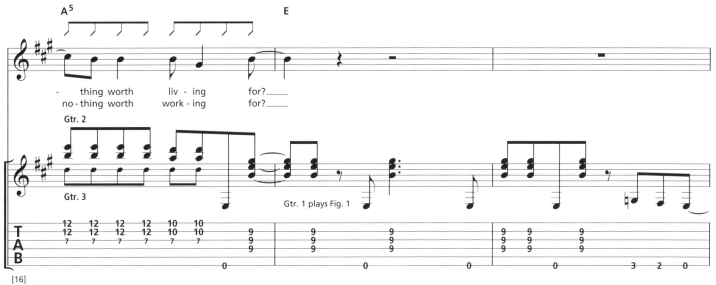

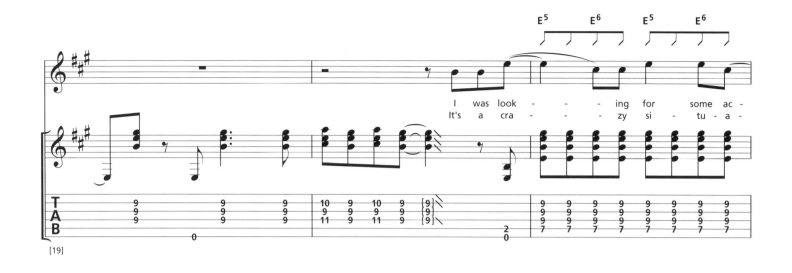

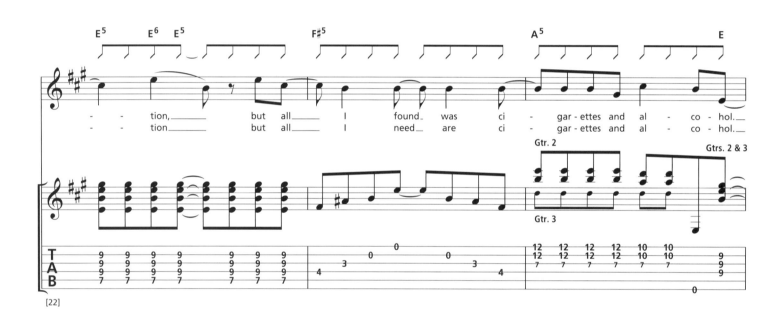

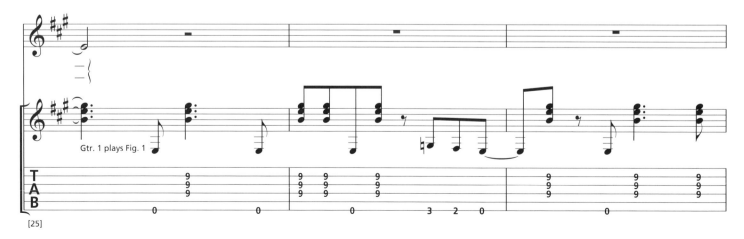

You could wait for a life - time,

to spend your days in the sun - - - - shine,___ you might as well do the white

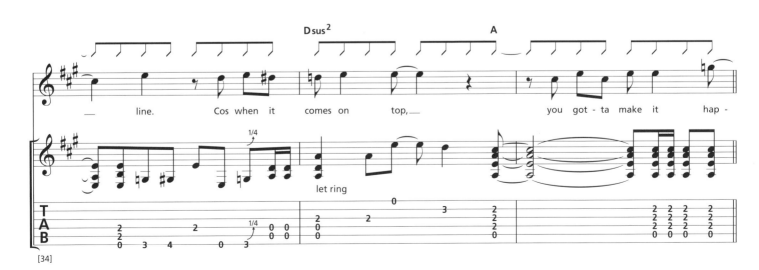

___ line. Cos when it comes on top,___ you got - ta make it hap -

let ring

Hot Rock Guitar Grade 3

55

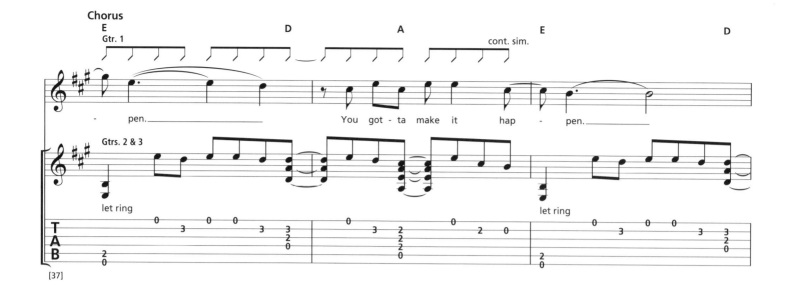

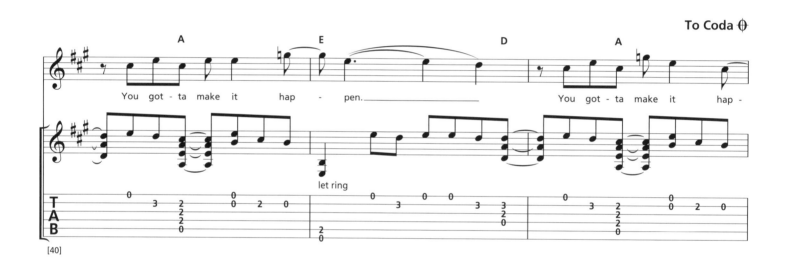

[47]

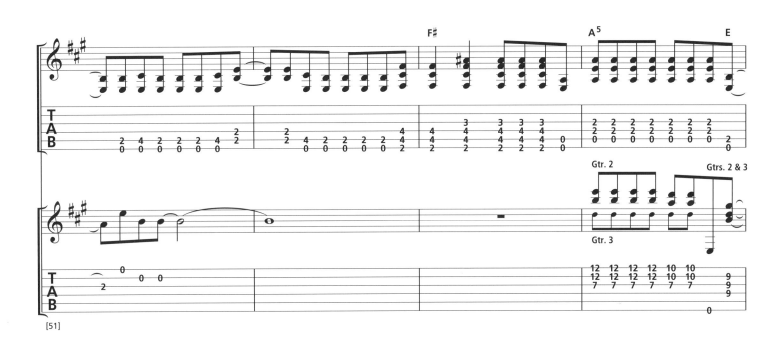

[51]

D.%. al Coda ⊕

2. Is it worth

Gtr. 1 plays Fig. 1

[55]

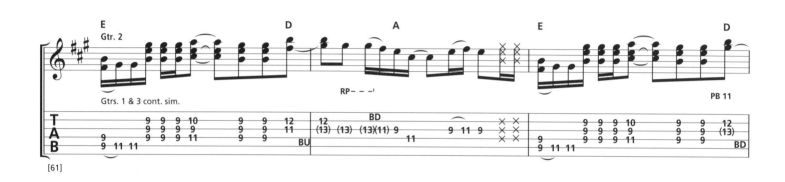

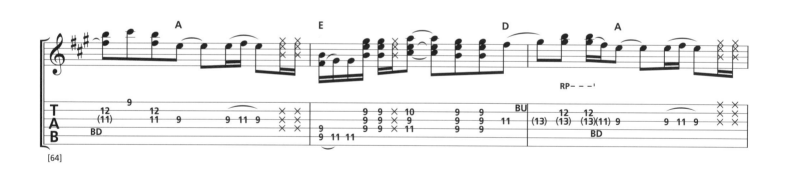

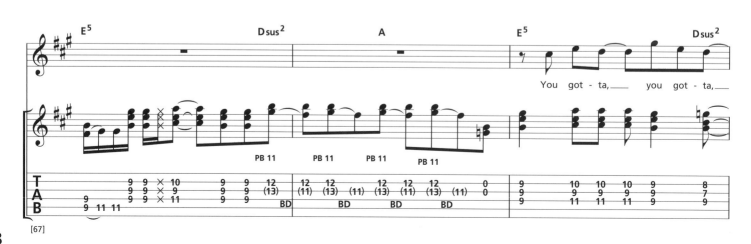

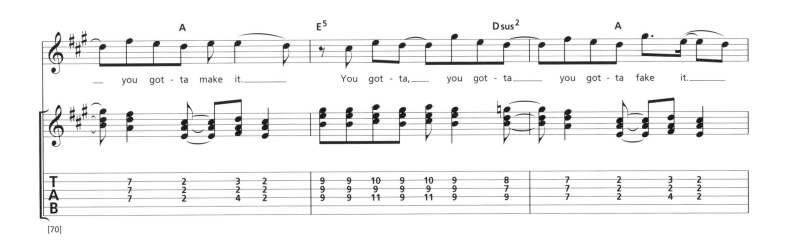

you got - ta make it._____  You got - ta,____ you got - ta____ you got - ta fake it.

[70]

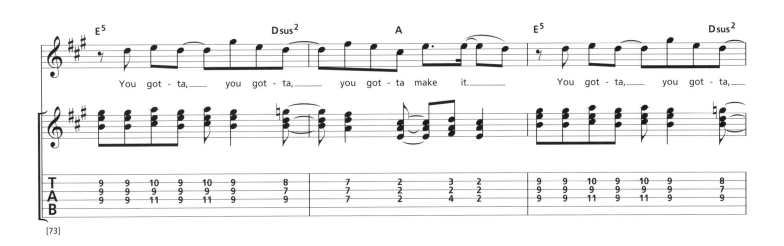

You got - ta,____ you got - ta,____ you got - ta make it._____  You got - ta,____ you got - ta,____

[73]

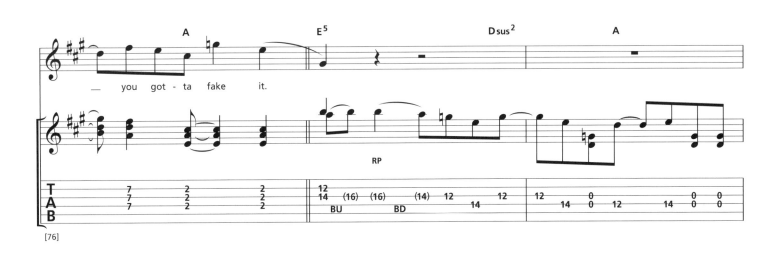

____ you got - ta fake it.

[76]

[79]

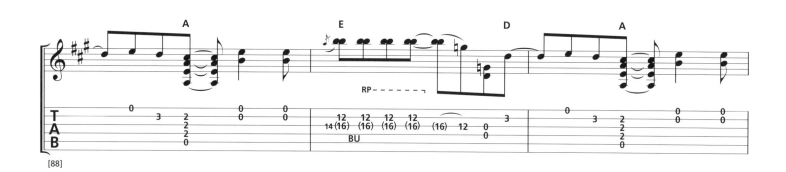

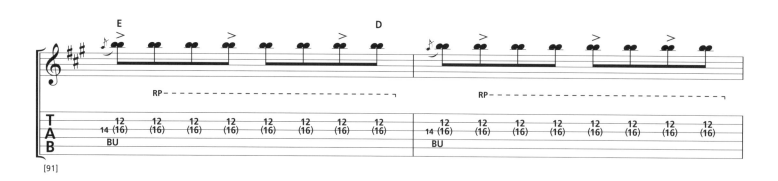

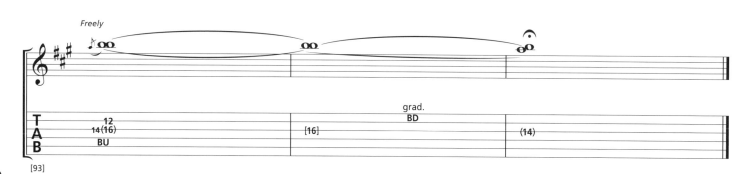

## Foundation Players

The majority of this song is suitable for players of this standard, though some beginners may find some of the syncopated (off beat) rhythms take a little while to master and the haphazard guitar solo may require some simplification to make it easier to comprehend.

### Bars 91–92 | *Accents*

An accent sign is placed above or below a note head. When you see this sign you should accent the marked note by playing it slightly louder than the other notes in the phrase. In this phrase the same bend is repeated and the accents outline a specific rhythm that complements the backing.

## Intermediate Players

The majority of this song is well within the abilities of players of this level. The guitar solo is a good study in pentatonic lead playing and will take a reasonable amount of practice to perfect.

### Bar 58 | *D.S. al Coda*

As you play through the song you will eventually come to a *D.S. al Coda* sign at bar 58 (Fig. 1). At this point you should go back to the 𝄋 sign at bar 13 and play from there. At bar 42 you will see a 'To Coda ⊕' direction, at this point you should jump to bar 59 (marked with a '⊕ Coda' indication) and play through to the end of the song. Navigating longer pieces like this will take some practice, but after a while following these kinds of performance directions become second nature.

### Bars 69–77 | *Shifting chord shapes*

At first glance it looks as if there quite a lot of different chords to learn in this section. However, it's actually the same two chord shapes played in three different fretboard positions. Play the first shape with your first finger barred across the second, third and fourth strings. The second shape is played by placing the second finger on the second string and the third on the fourth string.

### Bars 45–46 | *Semitone bends*

Semitone bends are often 'overbent' by inexperienced players who are used to the whole tone bends found in pentatonic solos. Play the target note (the note in brackets) before you attempt the bend. This will help with the accuracy as the target note is fresh in your memory.

### Bar 39 | *Let ring*

The 'let ring' direction indicates that the rhythm notation is only a guide to when the notes *start*, not how long they last. Once you have played the notes as written, let them ring for as long as practically possible. The music is consequently easier to read.

### Bars 77–95 | *Unison bends*

There are many unison bends throughout Noel Gallagher's guitar solo. A unison bend is where one note is fretted normally and a note on the next lowest string is simultaneously bent until it reaches the pitch of the un-bent note. Practice the bend slowly and you will be able to hear the change in pitch of the bent note (Fig. 2). If you have a floating bridge (where the bridge of your guitar 'floats' above the body of the guitar) the two notes will never sound exactly in tune as bending the note up causes the floating bridge to raise slightly which will cause the un-bent note's pitch to drop.

## Advanced Players

This song should pose few problems for advanced players. Players who are looking for a further challenge should replace the outro solo with one they have composed themselves or an improvisation that is in keeping with the original style.

### Bars 61–68 | *Oblique pre-bends*

This awkward bend is executed by playing the 12th fret at the second string with the fourth finger. The third string should be pre-bent using the third finger supported by the first and second fingers. Both strings should then be played and the bent note released. This technique will take some time to master, so don't be discouraged if it takes longer than you think it really should.

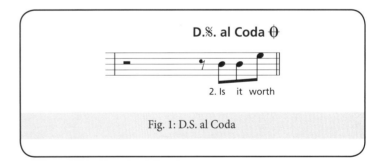

Fig. 1: D.S. al Coda

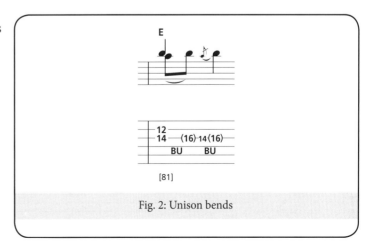

Fig. 2: Unison bends

# Golden Touch

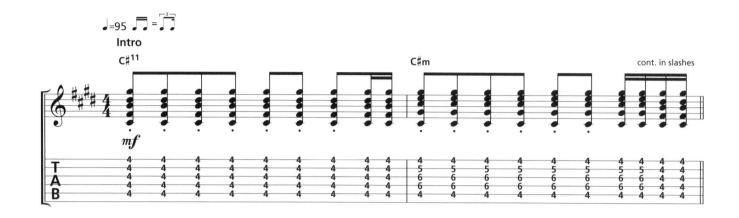

## Razorlight

Words & Music by Johnny Borrell

1. I know a girl___ with the gol - den touch,___
2. That kind of girl,___ yes she's nev - er a - lone,___

she's got e - nough, she's got___ too much.___
you leave a thou-sand mes - sa - ges on her phone.___

But I know___ you would-n't mind.___
But you know___ you'll ne - ver get through,

[7]

You could have it all___ if you want-ed,
(And) you could have it all___ if you want-ed, (yeah),

you could have it all___ if it mat-ters so
you could have it all___ if it mat-ters to you.

[9]

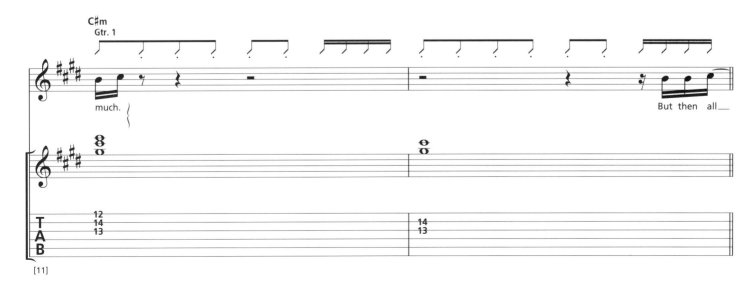

much.

But then all___

[11]

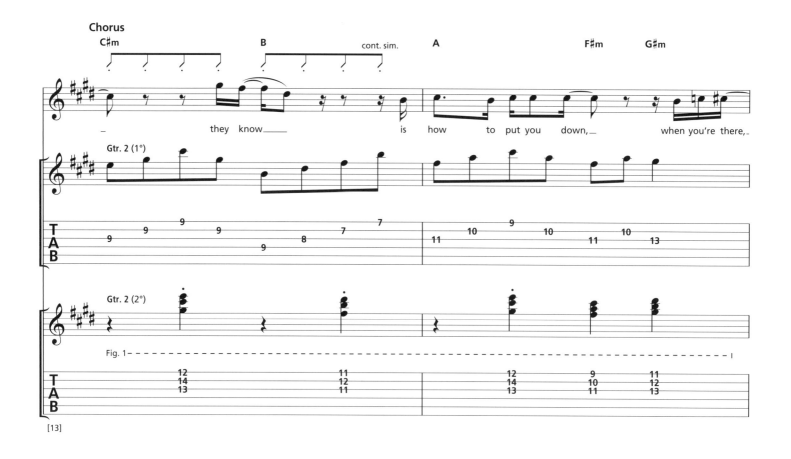

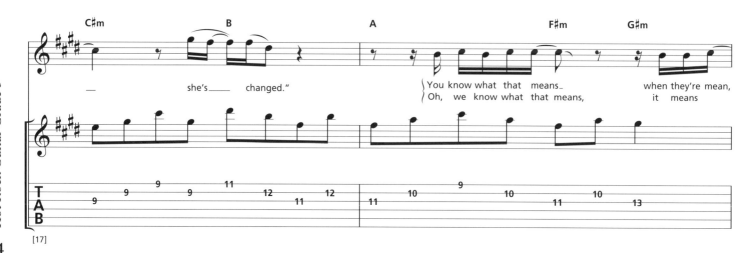

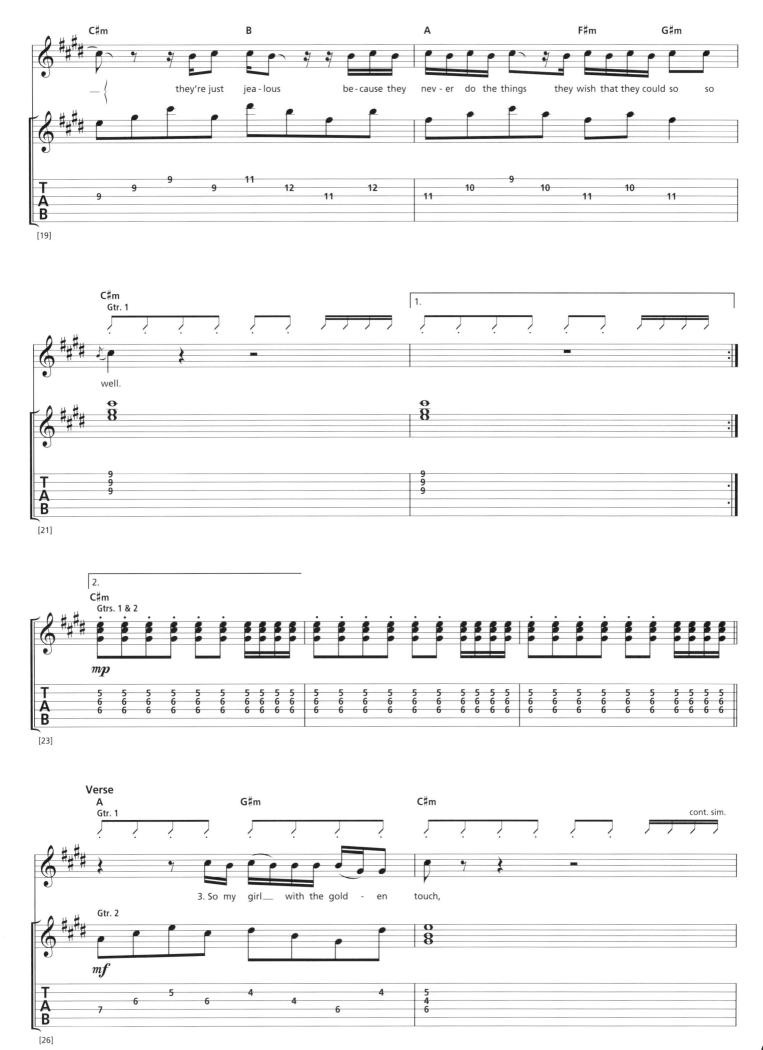

they're just jea - lous be - cause they nev - er do the things they wish that they could so so

well.

3. So my girl___ with the gold - en touch,

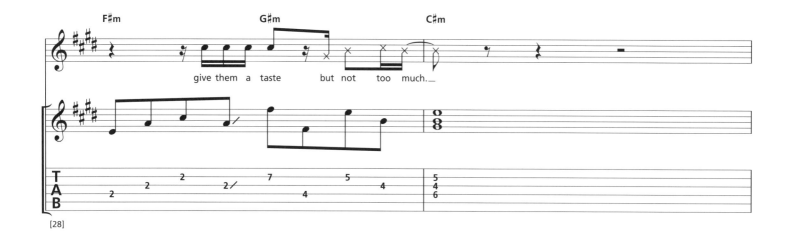

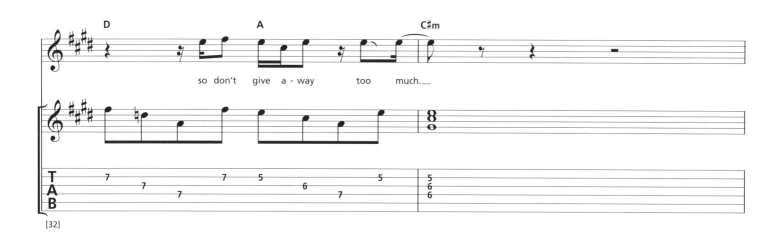

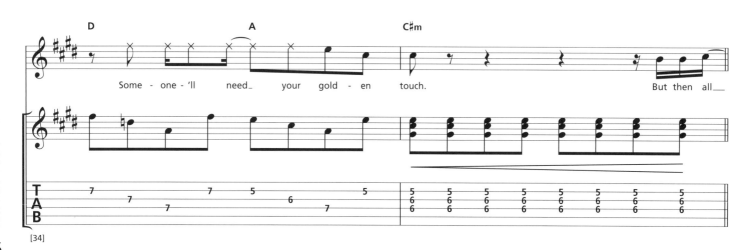

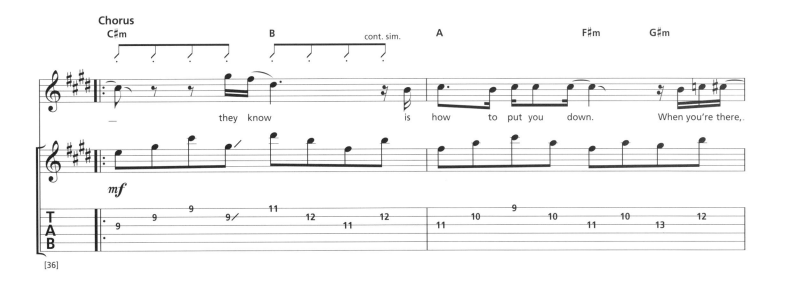

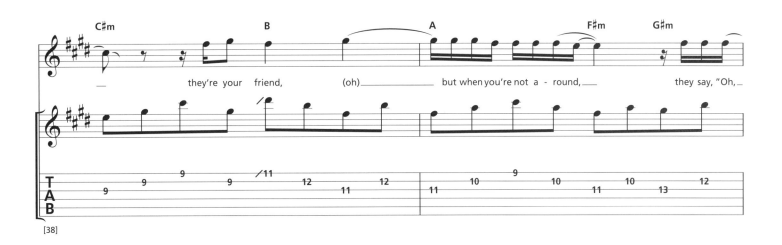

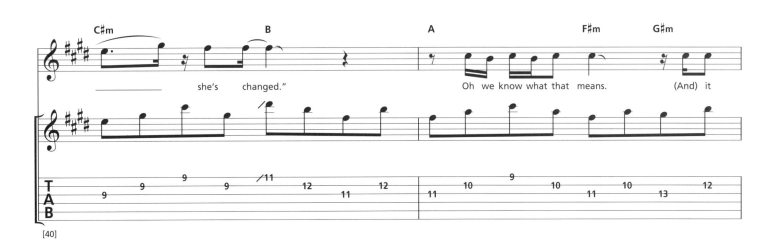

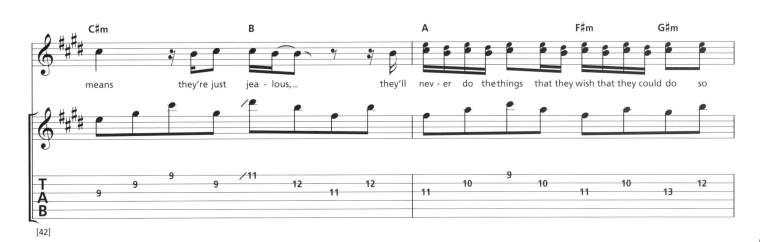

## Foundation Players

This is a challenging song for beginners to learn, though it serves as an excellent long-term study as it features barre chords, high-register chord voicings, unusual picking patterns and staccato rhythm parts.

### Bar 7 | *Slash chords*

A 'slash chord' indicates when a chord uses a bass note that is not the root note of the chord. The information to the left of the slash is the name of the chord, while the information to the right of the slash is the bass note. The B♭5/F chord in bar 7 indicates the chord is a B♭5 powerchord with an F note in the bass.

### Bar 44 | *Crescendo*

The 'crescendo' marking indicates you should gradually increase the volume of the notes underneath the sign (Fig. 1). A crescendo direction can cover any amount of time. In this instance it covers two bars.

### Bars 44–45 | *First and second time bars*

The first and second time bars in the main riff indicate the first time you reach the end of bar 43 you should play bar 44. The second time you reach the end of bar 43 you should miss out bar 44 and play bar 45.

### Bar 51 | *Fermata*

The note in bar 1 should last four beats. However it is marked with a 'fermata' which means you should hold the note for longer than the specified duration. As the fermata is above the final chord of the song, this means you can silence the chord when you feel the time is right.

## Intermediate Players

Despite the rhythmic simplicity of 'Golden Touch', this is actually a challenging piece for players of this level to learn. The rhythm parts require a great deal of endurance to perform and the unusual chord shapes combined with both the staccato chord stabs and intricate picking patterns means that any fretting errors will be exposed.

### Bars 1–4 | *Staccato Chords*

The dots above the eighth notes in bars 1–4 indicate they should be played 'staccato' meaning 'short and detached'. To achieve this sound, release the pressure on the strings as soon as you play the note.

### Bars 15–20 | *The 'next note' method*

There are lots picking options for this section. One popular method is alternate picking, another is the 'Next Note' method. Start the first chord with a downstroke then pick each note in the direction of the note that follows it (Fig. 2). Using a consistent approach like this will increase fluency.

### Bars 3–8 | *Consistent arpeggios*

Aim for a consistent sound where each note is played at the same volume. Watch particularly for the first upstroke in the sequence (the third, sixth and 11th notes of the riff) as many players have a tendency to play this note too hard.

### Bars 3–5 | *Rhythm notation*

If you have worked your way through the main guitar parts, or are playing the song with another guitarist, you might like to play the rhythm notation above the stave. This is the part played by the second and third guitars and complements the first. Start by strumming the chords without following the rhythm notation, then add the rhythms in when you are more comfortable with the changes.

## Advanced Players

This is a fairly straightforward track for advanced players. The focus should be on creating a consistent, professional performance that as a good sense of style, good timing and is flawlessly executed.

### Bar 36 | *Cont. Sim.*

The *cont. sim.* direction means you should continue playing in a similar manner, but that the part may be varied slightly. These variations are usually rhythmic.

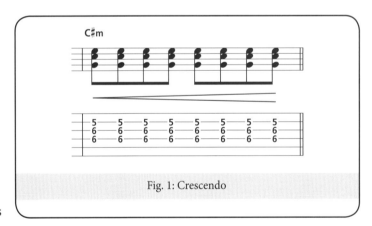

Fig. 1: Crescendo

Fig. 2: The 'next note' method

# Hey Joe

## Jimi Hendrix Experience

Words & Music by Billy Roberts

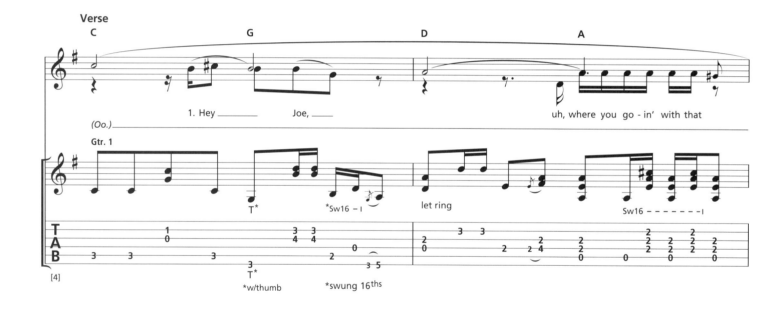

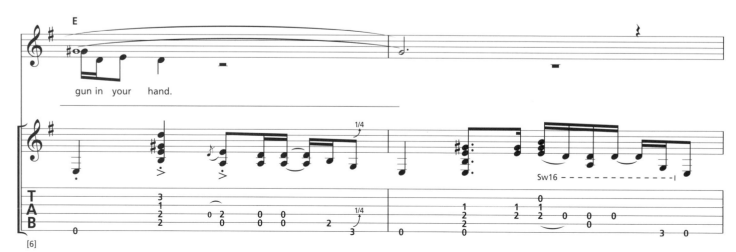

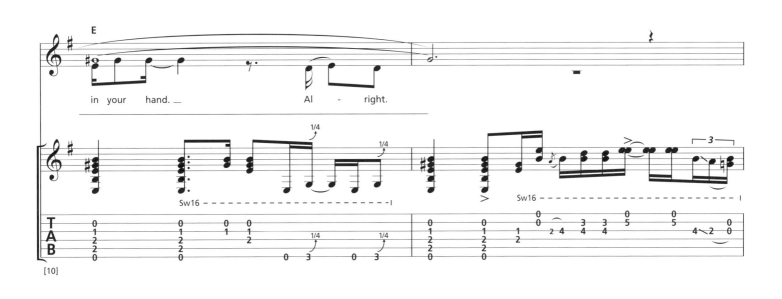

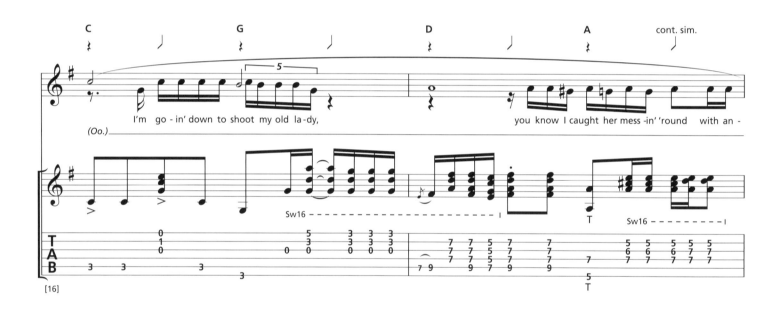

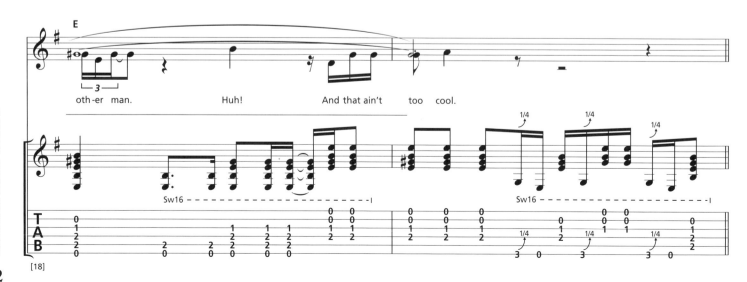

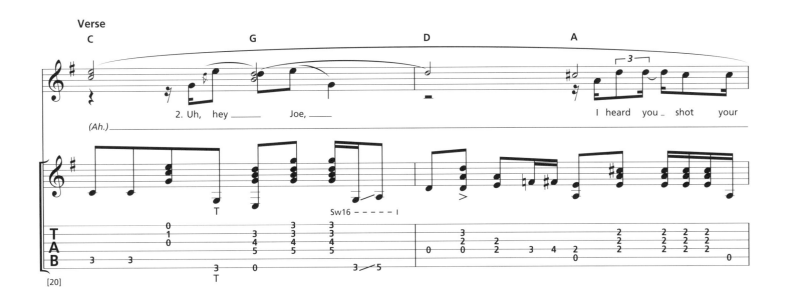

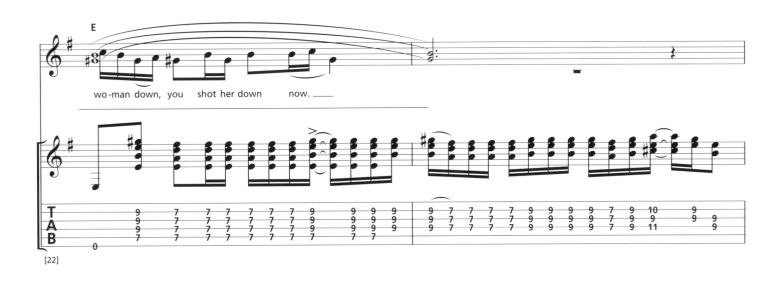

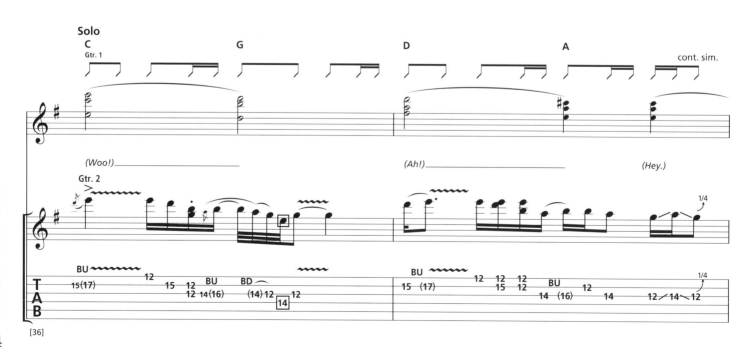

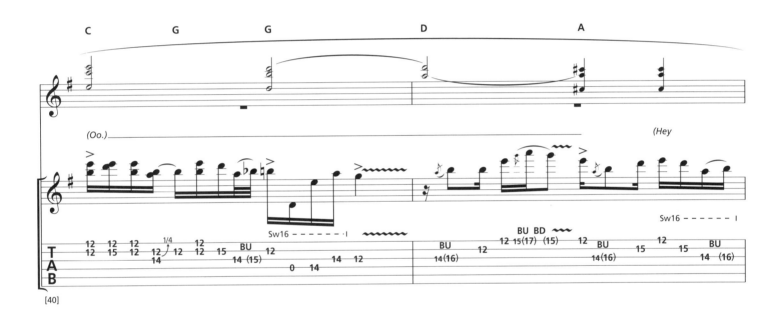

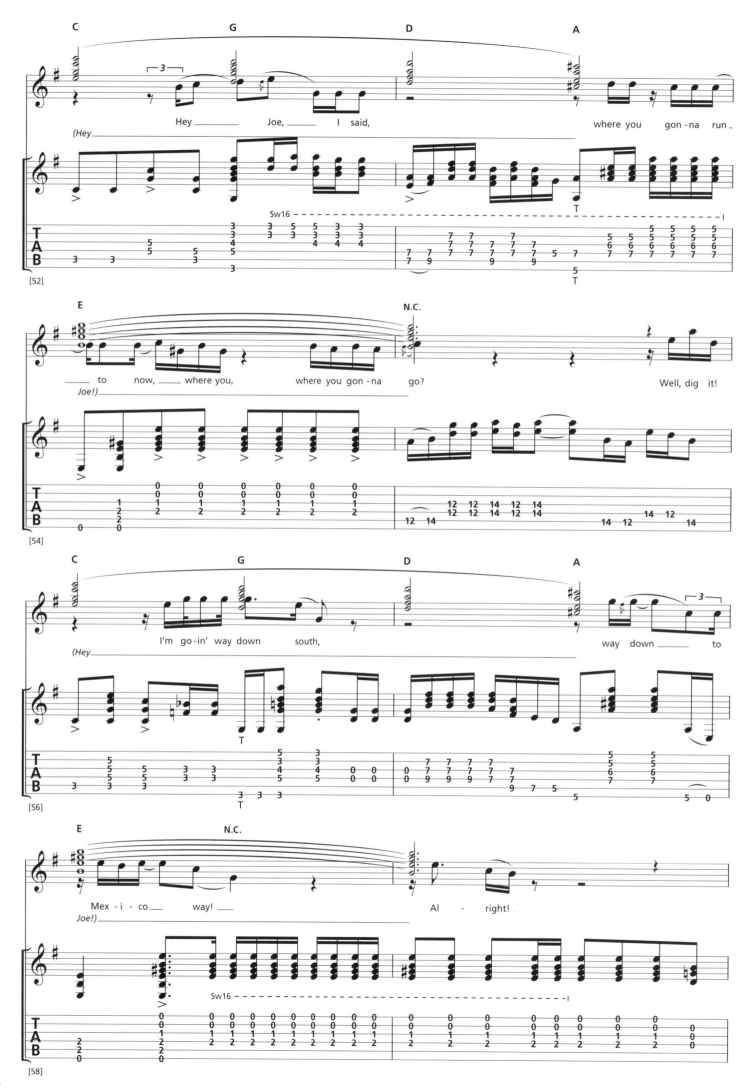

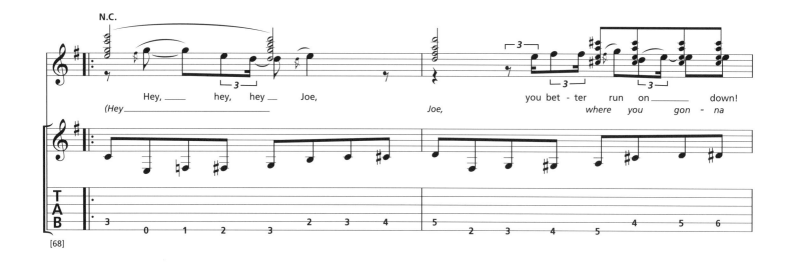

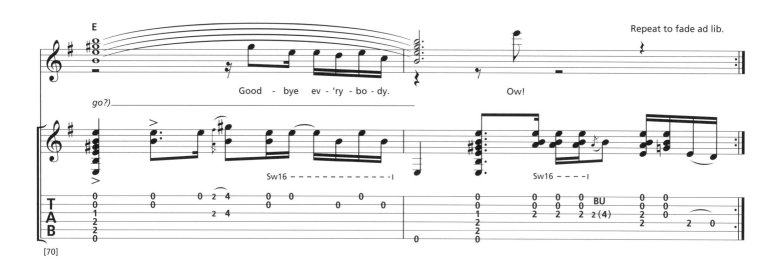

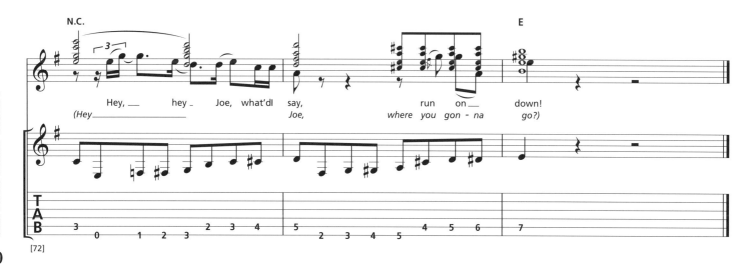

## Foundation Players

Jimi Hendrix's improvisational rhythm and lead style makes 'Hey Joe' a difficult song for players of this level to learn. Rather than attempting to learn this version of the song, Foundation players may have more success with the more structured and simplified exam version.

**Bars 1–74 | *Sixteenth note strumming***
To play this fluently requires sixteenth-note strumming. This is where the picking hand strums four times for every beat of the bar. The pick doesn't strike the string four times per beat: some of these will be 'ghost' strums.

**Bars 1–74 | *Ghost strums***
Keeping your hand in a constant motion between chord hits helps to make rhythm parts more fluent. When you don't want to strike the strings move your pick a small amount away from them, these are called 'ghost strums'.

## Intermediate Players

This is an excellent song for players of this level to learn. Jimi Hendrix's rhythm style was highly influential and 'Hey Joe' is an excellent example of it and worthy of study by *all* guitarists regardless of the style of music they are primarily interested in. The lead solo is also a fine study in blues rock.

**Bars 1–74 | *Complex rhythms***
It can sometimes be counter-productive to try and count complex-looking rhythms. While they can be intimidating in notation, learning the phrase aurally can be a much easier and instinctive way of learning something that Hendrix never intended to write down.

**Bar 36 | *Fretting hand tap***
The penultimate note of bar 36 is played by articulating the note at the 14th fret with the third finger without picking it (Fig. 1). This technique is sometimes referred to as a 'hammer-on from nowhere', a phrase first used by legendary guitarist Eddie Van Halen.

## Advanced Players

Players of this level will find this a rewarding song to learn and perform. There are several advanced techniques to master and if you are to perform this song in the true spirit of Hendrix, there are numerous opportunities for you to hone your improvisational skills.

**Bars 1–74 | *Performing songs note-for-note***
Hendrix's style is very improvisational and he never played his songs live the same was they were record and was even quoted as saying that people should go home and listen to the record if that was what they wanted to hear. With that in mind, treat the full transcription as a guide and, after working through Hendrix's original ideas, use the song's guitar playing as a springboard for your own improvisations.

**Bar 3 | *Chordal fills***
Hendrix's chordal style was based on embellishing basic barre chord shapes with additional notes. Often these were articulated with fast hammer-ons and pull-offs. Fig. 2 shows some of his favourite note combinations.

**Bar 4 | *Using the thumb to play bass notes***
This way of playing barre chords was one of Jimi Hendrix's signature techniques. The top four strings are played like an open position F chord and the thumb is hooked over the top of the neck to play the bass note. This technique frees up the fourth finger for playing chordal embellishments like those found throughout 'Hey Joe' (see *chordal fills*).

**Bar 36 | *Applying vibrato to bends***
This advanced technique requires a lot of control to articulate. First focus on getting the initial bend to sound in tune then add vibrato. Some players apply vibrato by releasing the bend a *tiny* amount and returning it to it's 'in tune' position. Others prefer to apply vibrato from the in tune position in the same way you do to an unbent string. Experiment with both approaches and see which you prefer.

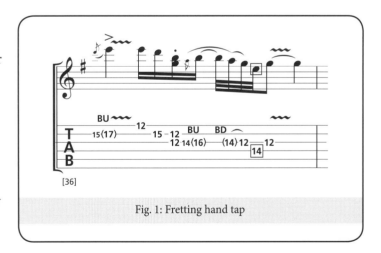

Fig. 1: Fretting hand tap

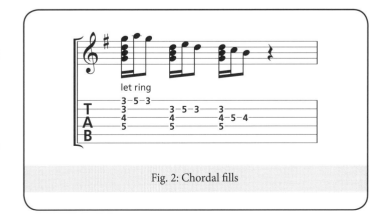

Fig. 2: Chordal fills

# Paranoid

## Black Sabbath

Words & Music by Ozzy Osbourne, Tony Iommi, Terry 'Geezer' Butler & Bill Ward

1. 𝄋.
C5
D5
E5
PM
(PM)
On 𝄋 Gtr. 2
To Coda ⊕
2.
Chorus
Can you help me
oc - cu - py my brain?
Oh
yeah.
[13]
[16]
[19]
[21]
[25]

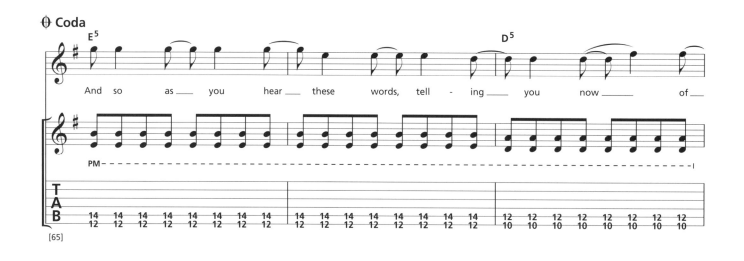

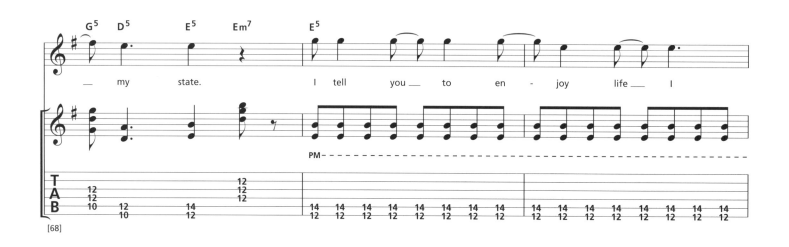

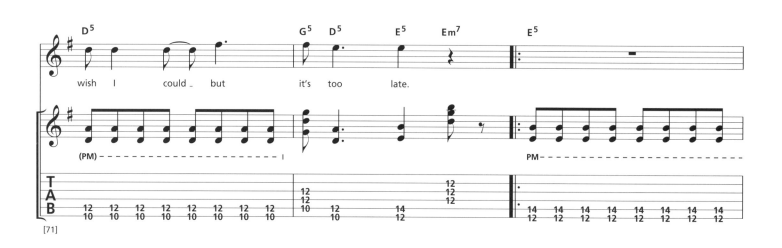

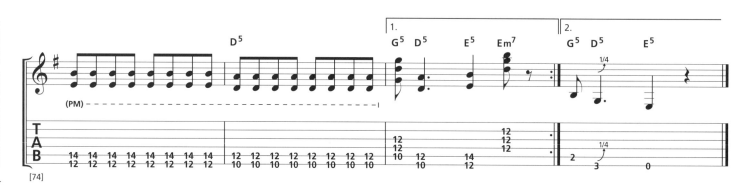

# Notes On The Full Transcription

## Foundation Players

The full version of 'Paranoid' is similar in standard to the exam version. Although the song is longer there are no extra parts apart from the full 16-bar solo, which is fairly demanding and will serve as a good long-term study for more experienced players.

**Bars 1–4** | *Consistent hammer-ons*

It's very common for inexperienced guitarists to rush hammer–ons and not allow the first note to sound for the correct amount of time. All the notes in this bar should be the same length.

**Bars 1–4** | *Grace notes*

Grace notes are very short notes used to embellish melodies and riffs. They have no timing value of their own, and are played as quickly as possible without interrupting the rhythm or flow of the music. They are represented in the tab by slightly smaller numbers than 'normal' notes. In this song they appear in the intro riff and the guitar solo (Fig. 1).

**Bars 1–77** | *Picking Stamina*

Playing all down strokes at 165 bpm for around three minutes is a challenge for a player of any ability. Examine your picking action and look to eliminate as much excess motion as you can. Try to stay relaxed as you play, even if you feel the tempo is getting on top of you, as unwanted tension drains energy quickly and will speed up fatigue.

**Bars 13–21** | *First and second time bars*

The first and second time bars in the main riff indicate the first time you reach the end of bar 12 you should play bar 13. The second time you reach the end of bar 12 you should miss out bar 13 and play bar 14.

**Bar 64** | *D.S. al Coda*

As you play through the song you will eventually come to a *D.S. al Coda* sign at bar 64. At this point you should go back to the 𝄋 sign at bar 13 and play from there. At bar 20 you will see a 'To Coda ⊕' direction, at this point you should jump to bar 65 (marked with a '⊕ Coda' indication) and play through to the end of the song. Navigating longer pieces like this will take some practice, but after a while following these kinds of performance directions become second nature.

## Intermediate Players

Most of this song will be well within the abilities of an intermediate player, although the guitar solo will take a little time to get up to speed.

**Bars 49–53** | *Target Notes*

The key to good string bends is hitting the 'target note' accurately. This is the note in brackets. An effective exercise to build this technique is to play the target note *first* and then attempt the bend (Fig. 2). Aim to match the bent note with the target note you just played. This will take some practise to perfect.

**Bar 41** | *Vibrato*

Vibrato varies tremendously from one player to another: it is one of the most distinctive aspects of a guitarist's style. Whether your vibrato is fast and wide or slow and shallow, make sure that the movement it is even and consistent otherwise you'll sound out of tune. One way to practise vibrato is to do 'push-ups' with a metronome. Look and listen to how far you move the string in your normal vibrato action. Aim to move the string *exactly* this amount *every* time and in time. Set your metronome to around 80–100 bpm perform your normal vibrato action slowly in time with the metronome. Be sure not to exaggerate your normal action: you're aiming to build a consistent vibrato, not change your style. This will help your vibrato sing sweetly and, most importantly, sound in tune.

## Advanced Players

This is a fairly straightforward track for advanced players. The focus should be on creating a consistent, professional performance that as a good sense of style, good timing and is flawlessly executed.

Fig. 1: Grace notes

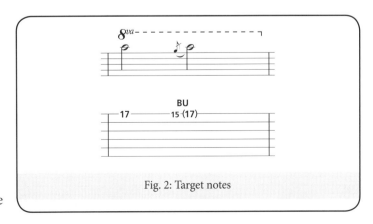

Fig. 2: Target notes

# Sex On Fire

## Kings of Leon

Words & Music by Caleb Followill, Nathan Followill, Jared Followill & Matthew Followill

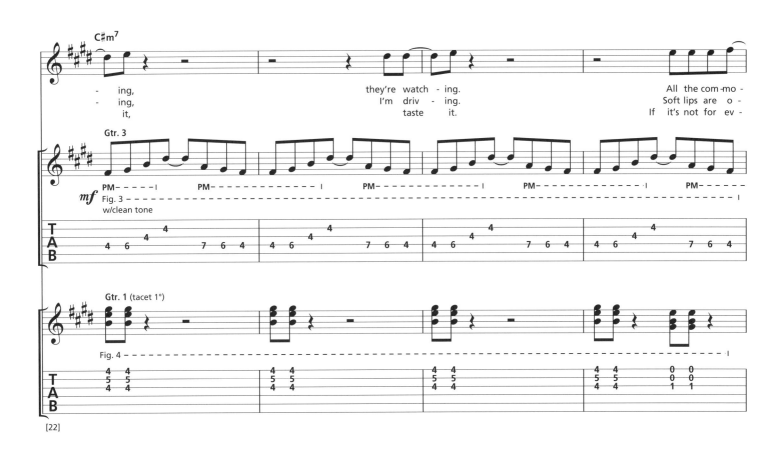

# Notes On The Full Transcription

## Foundation Players

The full version of 'Sex On Fire' is similar in standard to the exam version. Although the song is longer there are only a few extra parts. The syncopated intro is challenging because the drum part is fairly sparse and provides minimal help with timekeeping.

### Bars 38–40 | *Unison Bends*

A unison bend (Fig. 1) is where one note is fretted normally and a note on the next lowest string is simultaneously bent until it reaches the pitch of the un-bent note. If you have a floating bridge (where the bridge of the guitar 'floats' on the guitar body) the two notes will never sound exactly in tune as bending the note up causes the floating bridge to raise slightly which will cause the un-bent note's pitch to drop, so the two pitches will never meet.

### Bars 52–55 | *Playing octaves*

Fret the lowest sounding note with your first finger and the highest with your third or fourth fingers. Don't pick the notes individually: strum the two notes as though you were playing a chord. The underside of your first finger should naturally mute the fifth string (Fig. 2). If it doesn't, slightly adjust its position so makes light contact with the string to stop it ringing.

### Bar 84 | *Accents*

An accent sign is placed above or below a note head (Fig. 1). There are five different kinds of accent sign, but by far the most common is the one used in this piece. When you see this sign you should accent the marked note by playing it slightly louder than the other notes in the phrase.

## Intermediate Players

Players of this level should look to perform the song to a high level. The syncopated parts, while seemingly simple at first glance, must be played with a high level of accuracy, particularly where note lengths are concerned.

### Bars 38–40 | *Re-enforced bends*

String bending can be a physically demanding technique for the novice and experienced guitarist alike. Whenever you bend a string use all available fingers to push it up. This will give you more control and make it easier to hit the target note (the note in brackets). The bend in bar four should played using your third finger supported by your first and second fingers.

### Bars 41 & 42 | *First and second time bars*

The first and second time bars in the main riff indicate the first time you reach the end of bar 40 you should play bar 41. The second time you reach the end of bar 40 you should miss out bar 41 and play bar 42.

### Bar 50 | *D.S. al Coda*

As you play through the song you will eventually come to a *D.S. al Coda* sign at bar 50. At this point you should go back to the 𝄋 sign at bar 18 and play from there. At bar 40 you will see a 'To Coda ⊕' direction, at this point you should jump to bar 51 (marked with a '⊕ Coda' indication) and play through to the end of the song. Navigating longer pieces like this will take some practise, but after a while following these kinds of performance directions become second nature.

## Advanced Players

This is a fairly straightforward track for advanced players. The focus should be on creating a consistent, professional performance that as a good sense of style, good timing and is flawlessly executed.

### Bars 6–9 | *Correct note values*

This part's effectiveness relies on the chords lasting for only the notated length. To achieve this, release the pressure on the strings as soon as you play the note. Don't take your fingers all the way off the strings, simply stop pressing down. This will stop the note short, but won't produce any unwanted noise from the fingers leaving the strings. Attention to detail in these areas will elevate the standard of your performance.

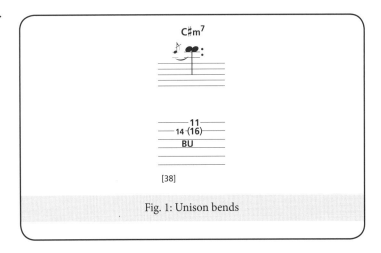

Fig. 1: Unison bends

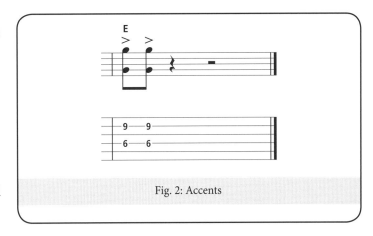

Fig. 2: Accents

# Steady, As She Goes

CD 2 Tracks 13 & 14

## The Raconteurs

Words & Music by Jack White & Brendan Benson

Hot Rock Guitar Grade 3

96

# Notes On The Full Transcription

## Foundation Players

While aspects of this song will be challenging for some beginners, it serves as a good introduction to several important elements of guitar playing. The verse and chorus riffs are perfect for learning barre chords and the choppy rhythms are a good way of building rhythm guitar skills.

### Bars 13–82 | *Chord strumming*

The is an exact transcription of the notes that the Raconteurs' guitarists played. Even they would not be able to re-produce a note-for-note duplication of the recorded performance. With this in mind, treat the number of string that are notated for each chord hit as a guide. Hold the chord shape down and strum freely. As long as you're playing approximately the right number of strings the part will be more than acceptable.

### Bars 26 & 31 | *First and second time bars*

The first and second time bars in the main riff indicate the first time you reach the end of bar 25 you should play bar 26. The second time you reach the end of bar 25 you should jump to bar 31.

### Bar 53 | *D.S. al Coda*

As you play through the song you will eventually come to a *D.S. al Coda* sign at bar 53. At this point you should go back to the 𝄋 sign at bar 23 and play from there. At bar 43 you will see a 'To Coda ⊕' direction, at this point you should jump to bar 54 (marked with a '⊕ Coda' indication) and play through to the end of the song. Navigating longer pieces like this will take some practise, but after a while following these kinds of performance directions become second nature.

### Bars 54–62 | *Alternate Picking*

These question and answer phrases are quite challenging at this tempo, so alternate picking (down up down up) is the most efficient picking action.

### Bar 63 | *Grace notes*

Grace notes are quick notes that precede a song's main melody or riff notes. They are represented by slightly smaller notes and numbers than used for 'normal' notes (Fig. 1). If held for too long it can interrupt the flow of the music, making it impossible to duplicate the original phrase.

## Intermediate Players

Most of this song will be well within the capabilities of intermediate players. Some work may be required to play the fast muted string rhythms in the later verses.

### Bars 28–30 | *Muted strings*

Place your fretting hand fingers over the string. Make firm contact with the strings, but don't push so hard that they are touching the frets or the fretboard. Use a sixteenth-note strumming action (four strums per beat) through this section to keep your playing fluent.

### Bars 54–65 | *Multiple voices*

No, we're not talking about voices in your head. Forget those for a moment and look closely at bars 54 to 64. While at first there may appear to be eight beats in each of these bars, a closer examination will reveal that there are in fact, two separate lines of music running concurrently within the same bar in the second guitar part! Each 'voice' is a separate guitar part, and these are made clearer by one part having it's note stems going upwards, while the other has it's note stems going downwards. Furthermore, one part (usually the less prominent sounding part) is often notated with slighly smaller notes.

## Advanced Players

This is a fairly straightforward track for advanced players, with only the fast muted string rhythms posing any real challenge. The focus should be on creating a consistent, professional performance that as a good sense of style, good timing and is flawlessly executed.

### Bars 82–87 | *Kbd. arr. for Gtr.*

This is a keyboard part arranged for guitar. If you want to play this interesting section (there are no guitars playing here) select a clean tone and fingerpick the part to duplicate the sound of a keyboard player who would play all the notes of the chord at the same time.

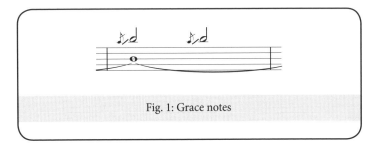

Fig. 1: Grace notes

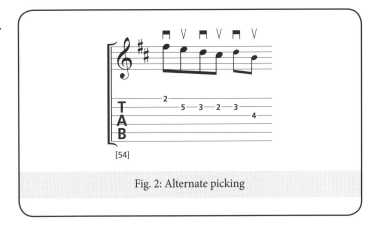

Fig. 2: Alternate picking

# Wherever I May Roam

## Metallica

Words & Music by James Hetfield & Lars Ulrich

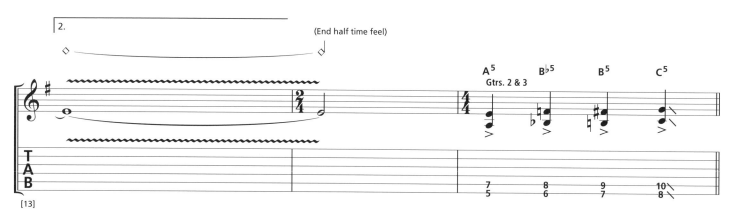

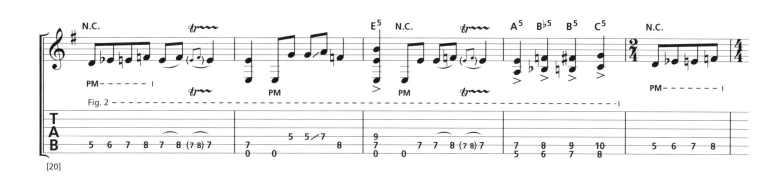

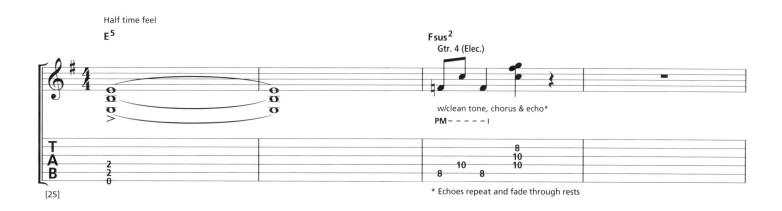

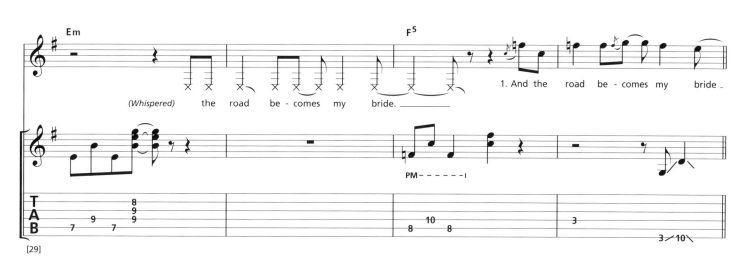

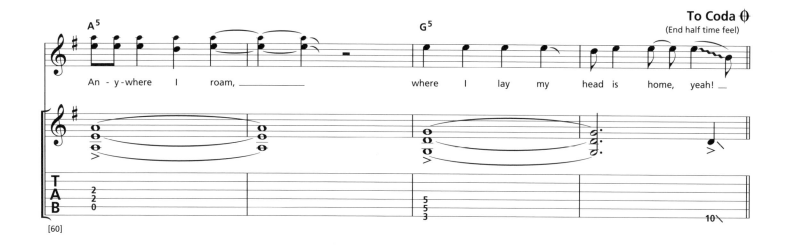

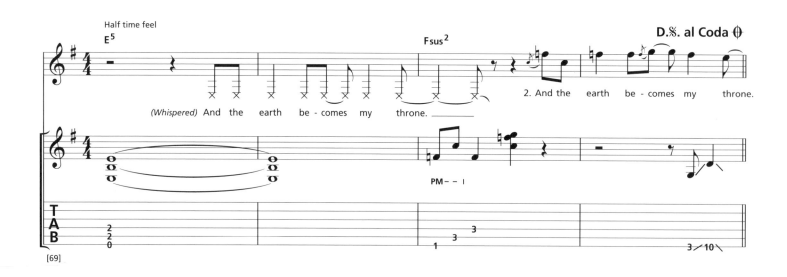

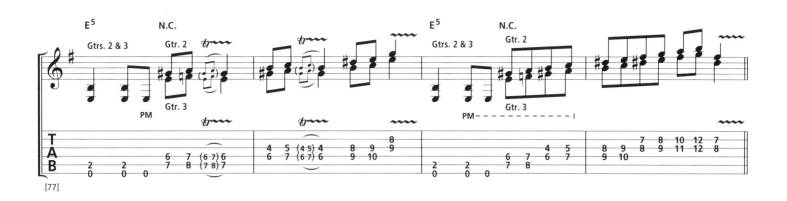

[77]

## Pre-Chorus

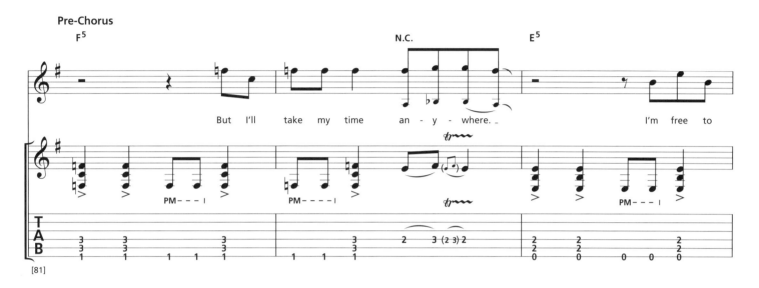

But I'll take my time an-y-where. _____ I'm free to

[81]

speak my mind. _____ And I'll take my find an-y - where.

cont. in slashes

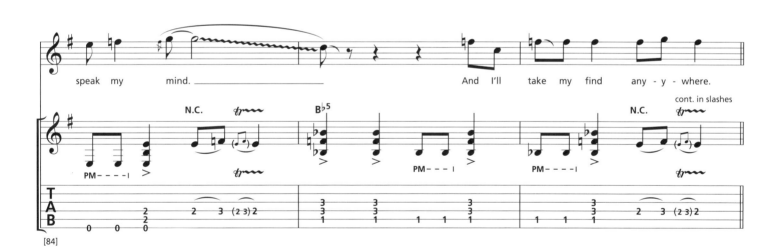

[84]

## Chorus
Half time feel

(End half time feel)

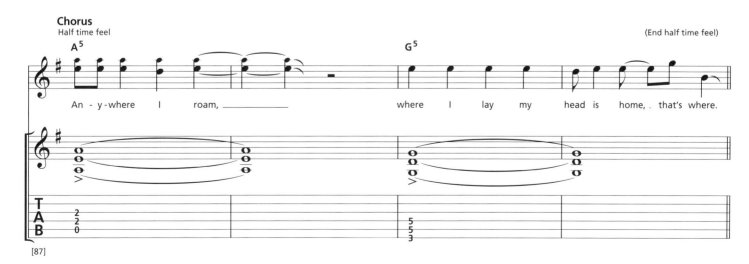

An - y-where I roam, _____ where I lay my head is home, __ that's where.

[87]

**Guitar Solo**

* Tap with edge of pick

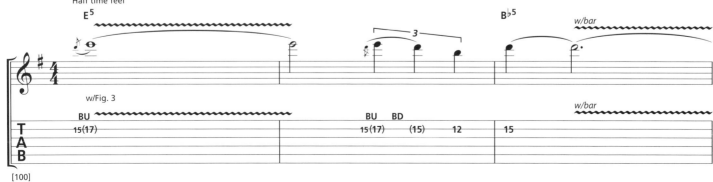

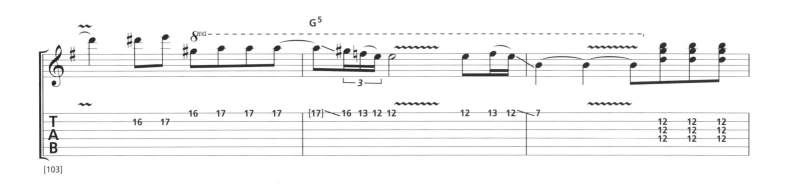

[103]

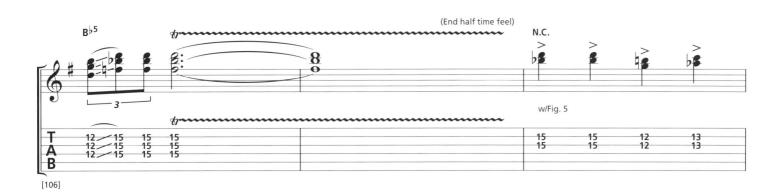

[106]

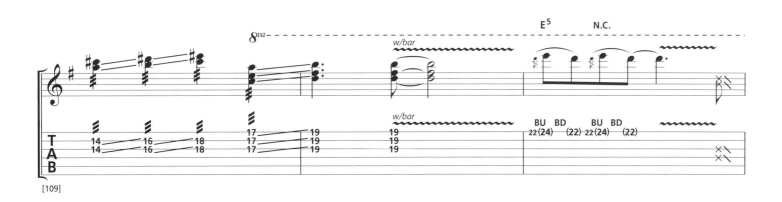

[109]

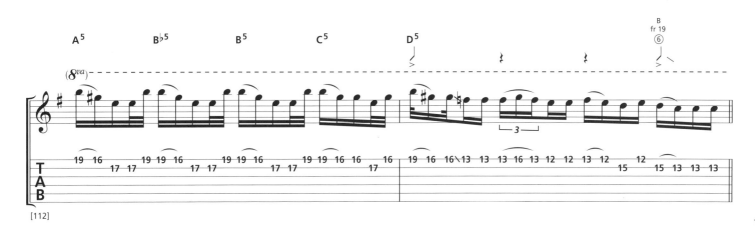

[112]

**Pre-Chorus**

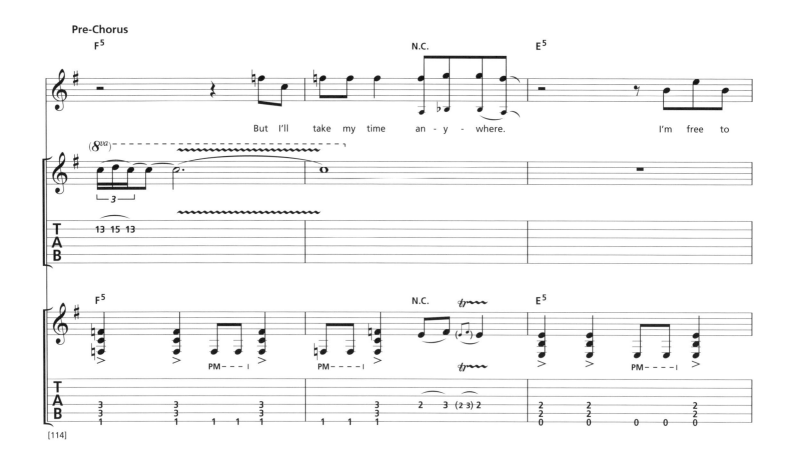

But I'll take my time an - y - where.    I'm free to

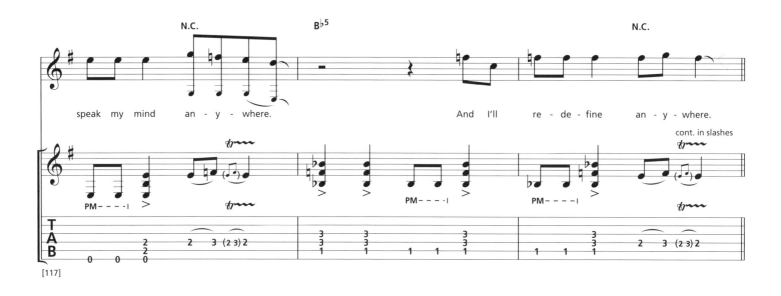

speak my mind an - y - where.    And I'll re - de - fine an - y - where.

cont. in slashes

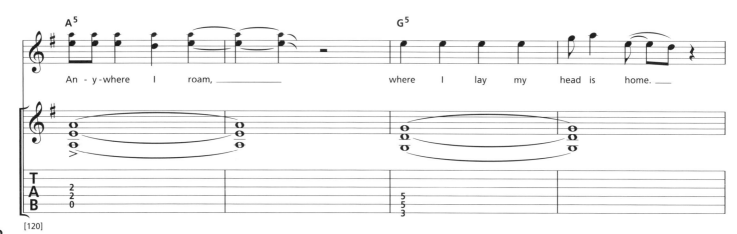

An - y - where I roam, _____ where I lay my head is home. _____

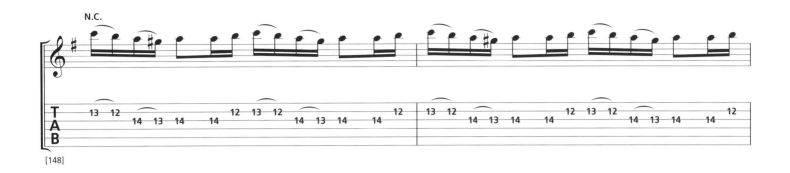

[148]

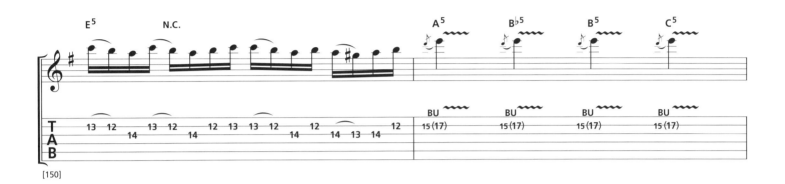

[150]

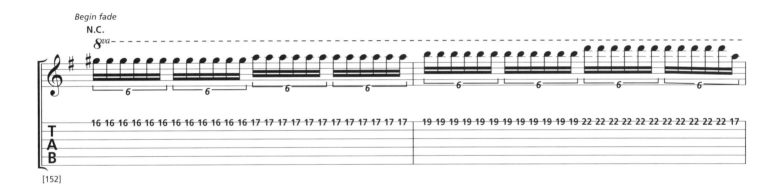

[152]

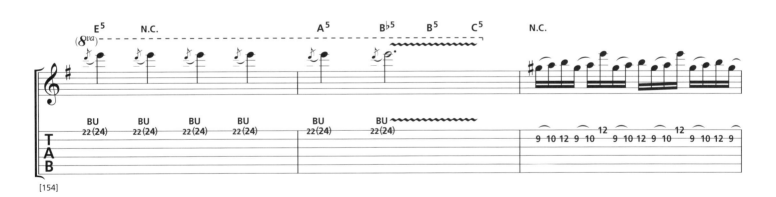

[154]

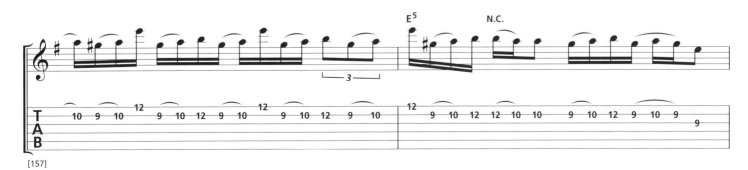

[157]

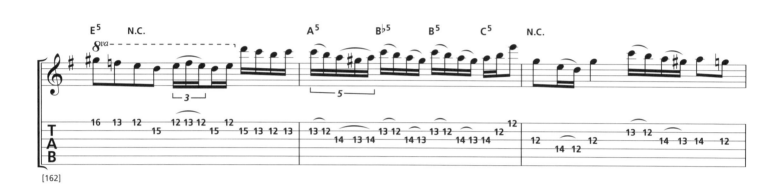

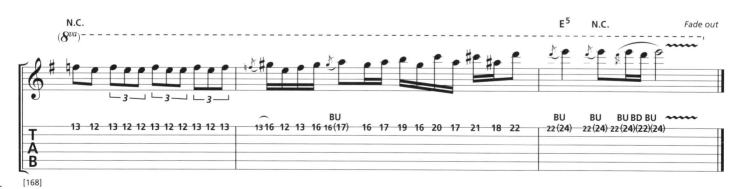

## Foundation Players

This a very challenging song for a player of this level. The song is quite complex with lots of different sections. More experienced players may find the rhythm parts a good long term study, but beginners may find the exam version a better option for them.

### Bar 5 | *Sliding octaves*

This part was originally played on two electric sitars and has been arranged for one guitar in this transcription (Fig. 1). You should approach slides octaves in the same way as playing powerchords and barre chords: lock your fingers in position and move the fretting hand as a unit rather than dealing with individual finger placement. The added difficultly of sliding octaves is that you must maintain pressure on the strings to keep the notes ringing. This may take some practice to get right, especially if you use the weaker fourth finger to fret the higher octave.

### Bar 13 | *Accents*

An accent mark is place above or below a note head. When you see this sign you should accent the marked note by playing it slightly louder than the other notes in the phrase.

## Intermediate Players

Intermediate players will find the rhythm parts easy to learn, but they will take more time to master. Metal rhythm guitar must be aggressive, yet accurate which takes considerable practise. The two guitar solos are very advanced, but some intermediate players may have success if they work on them as long term goals.

### Bars 1–7 | *Imitating a sitar*

While it's impossible to replicate the sound of the electric sitar used on the original version, slight adjustments to your technique and guitar tone will help mimic the sound for a more authentic performance. Select the bridge pickup for the brightest possible tone and pick as close to the bridge as you can, without adversely affecting your technique.

### Bars 77–78 | **Harmony trills**

This section features two guitar parts playing trills in harmony. You will need to play close attention to the part on the backing track so you synchronise with it, otherwise the two guitars will clash.

## Advanced Players

This is an excellent song for advanced players to learn. Aside from the precise rhythm playing required for an authentic performance of this song, the two guitar solos are technically very challenging and will take even the most experienced players some time to perfect.

### Bars 91–113 | *Wah Wah pedal phrasing*

Some players rock the wah pedal in time with the music, however, on the 'Wherever I May Roam', Metallica lead guitarist, Kirk Hammett uses the pedal to accent certain parts of his phrases to give the lead break a more vocal quality. While simple wah pedal movements are sometimes notated more complex pedal movements like those in the solo sections must be learned aurally.

### Bar 109 | *Tremolo picking*

The three slanted lines under the notes indicates the note should be tremolo picked. This is where notes are rapidly repeated. Technically, the three lines indicated the notes should be picked in a 32nd-note rhythm (the lines represent the tail from the 32-note notation), but your goal should be to produce a high speed stream of notes rather than precisely follow the prescribed rhythm. Start slowly, and gradually build speed as you become more comfortable with this technically demanding phrase.

### Bars 140–142 | *Complex rhythms*

It can sometimes be counter-productive to try and count high tempo, complex-looking rhythms. While they can be intimidating in notation, learning the phrase aurally can be a much easier and instinctive way of learning a phrase that the composer never intended to write down.

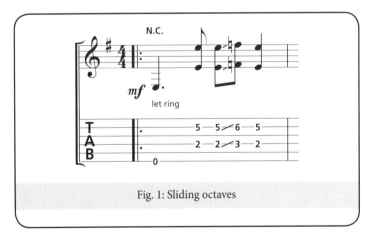

Fig. 1: Sliding octaves

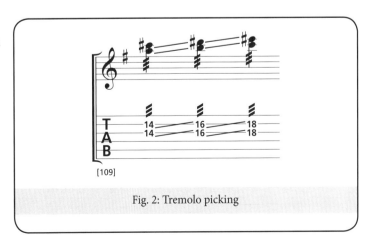

Fig. 2: Tremolo picking

# CD TRACK COPYRIGHT INFORMATION

## CD1 & CD2:

Ain't Talkin' 'Bout Love
(Lee Roth/Van Halen/Van Halen/Anthony)
Warner/Chappell North America Limited/Red Stripe Plane Music, LLC.

Cigarettes & Alcohol
(Gallagher)
Sony/ATV Music Publishing.

Golden Touch
(Borrell)
Sony/ATV Music Publishing.

Hey Joe
(Billy Roberts)
Carlin Music Corporation.

Paranoid
(Osbourne/Iommi/Butler/Ward)
Westminster Music Limited.

Sex On Fire
(Followill/Followill/Followill/Followill)
Bug Music-Music Of Windswept/Bug Music Limited/IQ Music Limited/Copyright Control.

Steady, As She Goes
(White/Benson)
Chrysalis Music Limited/EMI Music Publishing Limited.

Wherever I May Roam
(Hetfield/Ulrich)
Universal Music Publishing Limited.

# Guitar Notation Explained

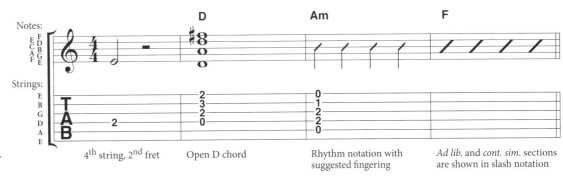

**THE MUSICAL STAVE** shows pitches and rhythms and is divided by lines into bars. Pitches are named after the first seven letters of the alphabet.

**TABLATURE** graphically represents the guitar fingerboard. Each horizontal line represents a string, and each number represents a fret.

4th string, 2nd fret    Open D chord    Rhythm notation with suggested fingering    *Ad lib.* and *cont. sim.* sections are shown in slash notation

## Definitions For Special Guitar Notation

**HAMMER ON:** Pick the lower note, then sound the higher note by fretting it without picking.

**PULL OFF:** Pick the higher note then sound the lower note by lifting the finger without picking.

**SLIDE:** Pick the first note, then slide to the next with the same finger.

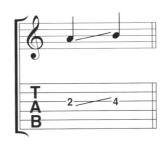

**STRING BENDS:** Pick the first note then bend (or release the bend) to the pitch indicated in brackets.

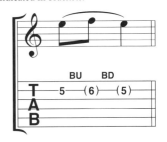

**GLISSANDO:** A small slide off of a note toward the end of its rhythmic duration. Do not slide 'into' the following note – subsequent notes should be repicked.

**VIBRATO:** Vibrate the note by bending and releasing the string smoothly and continuously.

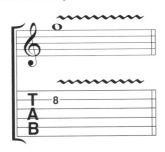

**TRILL:** Rapidly alternate between the two bracketed notes by hammering on and pulling off.

**NATURAL HARMONICS:** Lightly touch the string above the indicated fret then pick to sound a harmonic.

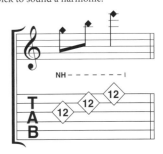

**PINCHED HARMONICS:** Bring the thumb of the picking hand into contact with the string immediately after the pick.

**PICK HAND TAP:** Strike the indicated note with a finger from the picking hand. Usually followed by a pull off.

**PICKING DIRECTION:** The first note is picked with a down stroke, the second with an up stroke.

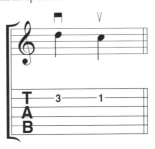

**QUARTER TONE BEND:** Pick the note indicated and bend the string up by a quarter tone.

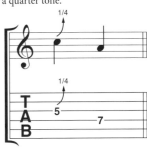

**PRE-BENDS:** Before picking the note, bend the string from the fret indicated between the staves, to the equivalent pitch indicated in brackets in the TAB

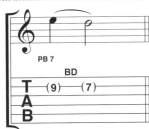

**WHAMMY BAR BEND:** Use the whammy bar to bend notes to the pitches indicated in brackets in the TAB

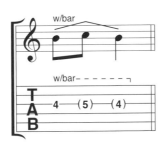

*D.%. al Coda*

*D.C. al Fine*

- Go back to the sign (%), then play until the bar marked *To Coda* ⊕ then skip to the section marked ⊕ *Coda*.

- Go back to the beginning of the song and play until the bar marked *Fine* (end).

- Repeat bars between signs.

- When a repeated section has different endings, play the first ending only the first time and the second ending only the second time.

# GRADE BOOKS

## Play the music you love AND get a qualification

**Guitar**
Debut to Grade 8

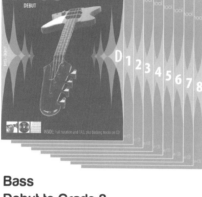

**Bass**
Debut to Grade 8

**Drums**
Debut to Grade 8

**Vocals (Male and Female)**
Level 1 to Level 3

**Piano**
Debut to Grade 8

**Band Based Keys**
Debut to Grade 5

rockschool Grade books come with eveything you need to take the exam

- 6 original tunes to choose from
- Standard Notation
- TAB for Guitar and Bass
- CD with full mixes and backing tracks
- Examples of the unseen tests
- Hints and Tips for each track

All our Grades are accredited by Ofqual, and Grades 6, 7 and 8 are worth UCAS points

# COMPANION GUIDES

## Arm yourself for success and demystify the technical side of Grade Exams with a rockschool Companion Guide

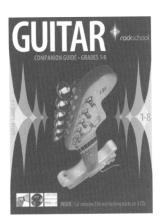

Guitar - Grade 1 to Grade 8

Bass - Grade 1 to Grade 8

A must for any music teacher or self taught musician, Companion Guides come with multiple examples of:

- **Sight Reading**
- **Improvisation & Interpretation**
- **Quick Study Pieces**
- **Ear Tests**
- **General Musicianship Questions**
- **Hints and Tips on the tricky sections**

Drums - Grade 1 to Grade 8

Band Based Keys - Debut to Grade 5

## GUITAR TECH COMPANION

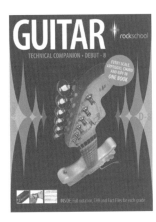

Guitar - Debut to Grade 8

Guitar Technical Companion takes the guesswork out of the technical side of your exam with technical exercises written out in full, detailed Fact Files and alternative fingering for each grade.

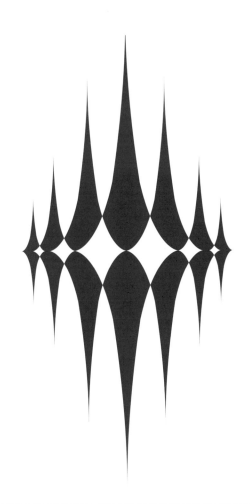

# QUALIFICATIONS

## Our practical diplomas are the next step for any Grade 8 musician wanting to start a career in teaching or performance

**Music Teaching Diploma**
Level 4

**Music Teaching Licentiate**
Level 6

**Teaching Diplomas**
are for self-employed teachers who want to develop their skills or musicians who want to go into music education

**Music Performance Diploma**
Level 4

**Music Performance Licentiate**
Level 6

**Performance Diplomas**
are for artists who wish to develop their existing performance skills and learn about the business and marketing side to being an independent artist

# VOCATIONAL QUALIFICATIONS

Vocational Qualifications offer practical, structured learning with the flexibility to specialise in different areas of the music industry.

Open to 16 -18+ year olds, Vocational Qualifications are a real alternative to GCSE, A – Level and BTECs.

**Music Practitioners**
opens the door to all aspects of the music industry from composition and performance to business and technology

**Creative Practitioners**
provides structured support for artists wanting to develop themselves and get started in the industry

**Music Educators**
is an introduction to music teaching that covers the theory and practical aspects of classroom teaching